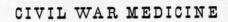

CIVIL WAR MEDICINE

Frontispiece. Hospital Steward (pharmacist) in the uniform of the Union (U.S.) Army during the Civil War. (Smithsonian Institution.)

CIVIL WAR MEDICINE

By

STEWART BROOKS

CHARLES C THOMAS • PUBLISHER
Springfield • Illinois • U.S.A.

Published and Distributed Throughout the World by
CHARLES C THOMAS • PUBLISHER
BANNERSTONE HOUSE
301-327 East Lawrence Avenue, Springfield, Illinois, U.S.A.
NATCHEZ PLANATION HOUSE
735 North Atlantic Boulevard, Fort Lauderdale, Florida, U.S.A.

With THOMAS BOOKS careful attention is given to all details of manufacturing and design. It is the Publisher's desire to present books that are satisfactory as to their physical qualities and artistic possibilities and appropriate for their particular use. THOMAS BOOKS will be true to those laws of quality that assure a good name and good will.

Printed in the United States of America
W-2

To
Sergeant Joseph Tyrrell Downey

Preface

THE CIVIL WAR started as a picnic and ended with compassion, but in between were four hideous years of twisted flesh, burning fevers, rampant pus, and oozing raw stumps. Never before had America faced even a hint of such wholesale agony and the way it responded to the occasion is fascinating history. In a very real sense the War Between the States brought forth a medical revolution and, perhaps above all, an awareness of public health. The terrible, swift scalpel became less terrible; and the dank, dirty, dingy pesthouse evolved into a pavilion of hope. Nursing, dentistry, and pharmacy also experienced a renaissance, and the art and science of military medicine was projected into the future. Though this small work is obviously not intended to detail all these things, the author hopes that he has presented the reader with an accurate, general account of what those festered years were really like along the lines indicated. In the areas of exceptional interest, however—for instance, surgery—the Official Records were carefully ransacked in an attempt to satisfy the peruser.

The author wishes to express his appreciation to the several institutions which supplied the illustrative materials, and to the people at Charles C Thomas, Publisher, for their enthusiasm, congeniality, and guidance. He thanks Natalie Ann Brooks, his wonderful wife, for just about everything in general and a well-fed index in particular.

STEWART BROOKS

Contents

Illustrations

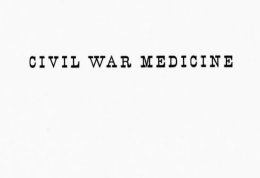

CIVIL WAR MEDICINE

CHAPTER I

Daniel et al.

FOR TWO days the big guns coughed loud and clear, but the only apparent effects were pocked masonry, dying embers, and a dead horse. There was also a feeling of good fellowship. When a between-shots Confederate envoy to the fort remarked to Major Robert Anderson that Sumter's fiery balls were falling wide of the mark, the commander replied, "Thank God for that!" Further, Confederate General P. G. T. Beauregard had inquired about the health of the men and sent along substantial volumes of brandy to boot! But this type of thing was not to go on.

In the wake of surrender, Major Anderson requested and received permission to fire a salute to the flag. At 2 PM (Sunday, April 14, 1861), Lt. Norman Hall gave the order and the guns along the disheveled parapet began to boom across Charleston Harbor. While the officers and men not detailed to the guns stood at attention on the parade, the colors set out on their downward journey. But the full salute—100 shots—never came about, for the fiftieth volley was followed by a terrible explosion. Debris and hot, acrid smoke filled the air and blood adorned steel and stone. Lingering sparks had prematurely set off the charge inserted by Private Daniel Hough and in turn a tongue of flame from this blast licked a nearby pile of cartridges.

The life of Private Hough, Battery E, 1st U.S. Artillery, was snuffed out in a flash, his right arm blown clean off at the shoulder. Of the dead, he would be the first. Private Edward Galloway, although tenderly cared for at a Confederate hospital in Charleston, died a few days later. He would be the second.

3

Private George Fielding, also taken to Charleston, recovered. Three other less-seriously wounded Federals were satisfactorily restored to health by Sumter's surgeon, Samuel Crawford.

Actually, Assistant Surgeon Samuel Wylie Crawford had already employed his medical skill on the day before the botched salute when Colonel Roger Pryor, one of the aides sent over by Beauregard to negotiate the surrender, helped himself to a sizable swig from a bottle in Crawford's quarters. If Pryor had only asked, the good surgeon would have reminded the parched Confederate that the stuff in the bottle was iodine. The hapless victim, with hands clutched to his burning throat, emitted an agonizing plea for help and thrashed about the room until Crawford finally managed to get him outside and apply a stomach pump. Thanks to the surgeon, the enemy was saved.

A few of the officers were somewhat disturbed that a Federal had interfered with a Confederate bent on suicide, but as Crawford pointed out, he was "responsible to the United States for the medicine in the hospital, and therefore could not permit Pryor to carry any of it away . . . " After all, this was a gentlemen's war and obviously slaughter had to be and would be, on occasion, tempered with brotherly love. This was especially so in the case of the colonel, because on the day before the encounter with that terrible Yankee elixir, Pryor had declined a signal honor when he replied to his thoughtful superior officer, "I could not fire the first gun of the war . . . "

This way of thinking, though, certainly could not be allowed to get the upper hand in real war—as a seasoning, perhaps, but nothing more. Besides, the picture was about to change and the beast in man would rise to the occasion. Eventually, the clumsy contraption proved it could and would maim people; torn young flesh would splatter the fields and orchards, and brave, bright blood would tinge the rivulets. Later, one nurse would say, "O God, such suffering it never entered the mind of man or woman to think of . . . "

According to Livermore, the Union had the equivalent

Figure 1. Staff buildings and wagons of Union Medical Department. (Library of Congress.)

of 1,556,678 three-year enlistments throughout the conflict, and the Confederacy somewhere in the vicinity of 1,083,000. No one will ever know for sure, but approximately 620,000 men perished, a figure of death that tops the total fatalities of all other wars in which Americans have fought. Of this number, 360,000 were lost to the North and 260,000 to the South.* A Civil War soldier's chance of *not* getting back home was about one in four, a terrifying statistic when we consider that his brother-in-arms during the Korean War could boast of "one in 126."

Surprising perhaps to the layman but not to the student of history, disease was the great killer of the war. As one soldier wrote, "These Big Battles is not as Bad as the fever." Of the Federal dead, roughly three out of five died of disease, and of the Confederates, perhaps two out of three. During the first year, a third of the Union army was on sick call, and probably an even higher figure obtained in the South. Intestinal infections, such as typhoid and "chronic diarrhea," and "inflammation of the lungs" headed the list. Indeed, diarrhea and dysentery became more vicious as the fighting progressed. Whereas typhoid killed a quarter of its victims during the first year of hostilities, the figure rose well above 50 per cent during 1865. At Andersonville prison, of 7,712 deaths between March 1 and August 31, 1864, 4,529 were ascribed to diarrhea and dysentery. The "prisons" of the Civil War were factories of disease and death; roughly, 19,000 Confederates and 26,000 Federals died under conditions that have never been surpassed in terror and brutality.

As regards the fruit of the gun, in the neighborhood of 94,000 Confederates and 110,000 Federals died from battle wounds, the chief killer being the rifled musket. The famous Springfield shot a one-ounce .58 caliber cylindro-conical lead bullet (the famed "minie ball") at a velocity of 950 feet per second. Although today this seems an ancient and highly ineffectual weapon, even as compared to the 1903 Springfield of World War I fame, it did the job well. At the usual battle range of 200-300

*Refer to "Introductory Note," p. 125.

yards, it was deadly. Actually, the Civil War was the first great conflict in which so accurate a weapon was employed, thanks to Captain Minié of the French army and to a self-educated genius from Sackets Harbor, New York, named Samuel Guthrie. Relative to war, Guthrie seems to have had a split personality. On the one hand, he experimented with the percussion cap, a detonating device for the rifled musket, and on the other, he discovered chloroform, the number-one anesthetic used throughout the War Between the States.

Although a poor second in regard to the number of men killed, the artillery proved of tremendous importance in overall tactics. It saved the Army of the Potomac at Malvern Hill and Antietam, and scared away would-be attackers on both sides throughout many engagements. The workhorse here was the 12-pounder, smoothbore "Napoleon" (a gun-howitzer) developed under the auspices of none other than Napoleon the Third. This piece could fire just about anything that happened to be lying around, but it performed best with canister, a nasty metallic concoction made by filling a tin can with bullets and sawdust. At ranges of between 100 and 200 yards, two or three Napoleons firing canister could atomize a line of Blue or Gray.

Those bent on the gory details of the bayonet and sword will have to take a look at the records of World War I, not those of the Civil War. Stonewall Jackson ("Give'em the steel") notwithstanding, the Yanks and Confederates thought little of the bayonet as a weapon, but did regard it highly as a pick, roasting spit, can opener, or what have you. Out of 7,302 Federal wounded delivered to the base hospital at Fredericksburg, for instance, only six were found to have been injured by sword or bayonet. Even so, it must be admitted the shiny twenty-inch spears and blades of Civil War vintage were awesome to behold and of psychological import. As one Confederate general put it, "The bristling points and the glitter of the bayonets were fearful to look upon as they were leveled in front of a charging line, but they were rarely reddened with blood . . . "

The nightmare of torturous sickness and wholesale death throughout the war is traceable to many factors, not the least being the way of life itself. In 1861, the boys of rural America were first and foremost rugged individualists. Hair, beards, and feet entered and left the army camps uncombed, matted, and dirty, respectively. What is more the boys, as in all "pre-antiseptic" wars, really let themselves go. Feet got dirtier, and habits in general became worse, if that were possible. During the first years, the camps about Washington itself were havens of pestilence; reeking garbage, open sewers, overflowing latrines, and dead cats and dogs were the rule and not the exception. Elsewhere, particularly in the West, the situation was as bad and often worse.

Superimposed upon this free way of life was the abominable recruiting system. Many recruits were too young and many were too old. Not infrequently the induction "physical" was a sham, for example, one doctor boasting he had examined 100 men an hour. Often, whole regiments would arrive in camp without having seen a doctor. According to a Sanitary Commission report of 1861, three-quarters of the soldiers discharged from the Union army should never have been enlisted in the first place. The situation was actually alarming and, during the first year and a half, dwarfed the murder of the battlefield.

And then, there were such things as bad clothing, bad water, and bad food. Although there was gradual improvement along this line in the North, conditions deteriorated in the South. Beans, salt pork, hardtack, and washy coffee were the bill of fare, if a person were lucky enough. Under less affluent circumstances a handful of corn or a piece of wormy hardtack had to do. The soldier who remarked, "Beans killed more than Bullets," apparently sized up the situation quite clearly.

Obviously, the Medical Department of both armies was faced with a stupendous and frightful task, and, in all fairness, performed reasonably well during the latter half of the conflict. (Indeed, Civil War medicine improved over the record of the Mexican War in which ten men died of disease for every man killed in battle.) It was a bloody picture from start to finish, because the materials and knowledge for healing the tattered body were either scarce or nonexistent. Medical know-how, especially in the surgical areas, frequently fell below the standards of the ancients. This was a time when the doctor rarely handled a clinical thermometer and the Harvard Medical School reportedly did not own a single stethoscope! In substance, then, the medicos in blue and gray had to do an impossible job with impossible means.

Of course, there was downright stupidity, too. Surgeon General Thomas Lawson thought it foolish to buy medical textbooks, and General Don Carlos Buell did not believe in a medical corps in the first place. Generally speaking, the line brass was lukewarm about such matters as calomel, scalpels, and ambulances, and in the beginning, Lincoln himself referred to the volunteer Sanitary Commission—the great savior of the war— as the "fifth wheel to the coach." Thus, to a degree, the men who ran the battles agreed with the gods of war; to wit, the business of war is to tear the body, not mend it. As one surgeon confessed to Clara Barton at Antietam, "I am tired of this inhuman incompetence, this neglect and folly, which leave me alone with all these soldiers on my hands, five hundred of whom will die before daybreak unless they have attention and I with no light but a five-inch candle."

If possible, the southern soldier was worse off than his enemy brother up north. Although the competence of the doctors and the organization of the Confederate Medical Department were just about the same, the dearth of clothing, food, and medical supplies in the South proved to be a significant hindrance to health and recovery. And as the war groaned on, the situation became more pathetic. Even at the half-way mark, some Confederates had to march in their bare feet. Among the Federals, on the other hand, the mighty mills and factories were coming to the fore; supplies of all kinds increased, even to the point of such a luxury as a dehydrated carrot.

If we regard the Civil War "as one vast experiment in the determination of how much injury the human body can endure," we must admit that the men on both sides stood up well. As a matter of fact, the statistics of survival as well as those of death are astonishing. The hospitals were filled and the battlefields littered with soldiers who, in the context of modern thinking, should have died, yet did not die. Indeed, one begins to wonder about the relative importance of dirty feet versus clean feet. Although Samuel C. Wright of the Twenty-ninth Massachusetts scarcely represented the rule, he certainly did point up an occasional trend. Wright fought in twenty-one battles; was wounded in the head by a shell fragment at White Oak Swamp, in both legs at Antietam, in the arm at Cold Harbor; was shot in the head and lost his right eye at the Battle of the Crater; had typhoid fever; broke a leg in an attempt to save a piece of artillery; and last, but perhaps not least, was run over by an army wagon in Kentucky . . . and Sam lived to be seventy-nine!

CHAPTER II

Hayfoot! Strawfoot!

SINCE THE men called to the colors commonly confused left with right, the drill sergeants tied a wisp of hay about the left foot and a wisp of straw about the right: " . . . Hayfoot! Strawfoot! Hayfoot! Strawfoot! . . . "

But the new recruits were not the only hayfoot-strawfoot people in this struggle, and the Medical Departments on both sides of

Figure 2. The United States Sanitary Commission during the Battle of Gettysburg, July, 1863. (Wide World Photos.)

the line were no exception by any means. At the outbreak of the war, the U.S.A. Medical Department was a fossilized organization headed by Surgeon General Thomas Lawson, a vastly incompetent and sick and dying man. It could boast scarcely more than a hundred doctors, a handful of clinical thermometers, and a gross or two of surgical kits of dubious quality; of hospitals and ambulances, there were none worthy of the designation. Though the Official Records imply this rickety setup was supposed to care for the needs of 15,000 or so men, one has excellent cause to wonder. More to the point, this department was to be the "guiding light" for the hayfoot-strawfoot volunteer doctors.

To make matters worse, when Lawson finally died in May, 1861, he was replaced by Clement A. Finley, another relic of the War of 1812. Surgeon General Finley not only had few ideas of his own, but went out of his way to squelch those of others. Typical of this man's thinking was his response to General Sherman's suggestion to build a hospital at Port Royal, South Carolina. Remarked the head medic, "The mild climate of South Carolina obviates the necessity for a hospital . . . "

It is certainly no stretch of the truth, then, to say that the Federals entered the war with medical capabilities below those of Imperial Rome. In the time of Hadrian, for instance, just about every legion and every warship had its own physician; and, interestingly, the Roman warriors had bandages, instruments, and military hospitals, some equipped with plumbing, kitchens, and pharmacies! Nevertheless, the people up north and those down south had things to settle and, ready or not, there would be real war. Things were looking up for those terrible war gods . . .

On the morning of July 21, 1861, Mr. Lincoln's volunteers under Major General Irvin McDowell engaged Beauregard's troops spread alongside a meandering stream called Bull Run. At first, the thing did not appear to be much of a fight, but by noon a vicious battle ensued. With the arrival on the field of Confederate General Joseph Johnston's men, the balance was upset and the tide was turned. Amid the hail of lethal hot steel, acrid smoke, and rebel yells, the Federals broke and ran for their lives.

The aftermath was terrifying. Although "medical directors" were present, they had no authority to tell anybody to do anything. Regimental surgeons refused to treat the soldiers of any regiment save their own, even though a poor creature cried or begged for someone to hack off a mangled arm or leg. Worse yet, the civilian ambulance drivers hired for the occasion had fled like scared rabbits at the sound of the first shots. Perhaps not a single wounded man made the twenty-seven mile trip back to Washington by ambulance. Men with shattered bones, no arms, eyes, mouth, or rectum did the best they could. Some walked, some crawled, and some, the lucky ones, were dumped into a good samaritan's springless wagon. This would be the first of thousands of such caravans of misery to come.

But getting back to the capital was no solid assurance that anybody in authority would be glad to see you. The hospitals, few and filthy, were already filled to the rafters and for days wounded soldiers wandered the streets and pounded on the doors. Some got in!

Back at Bull Run, meanwhile, the living squirmed among the dead, the only good sign being that an occasional gush had eased into an ooze. And by a quirk of nature some pulled through, especially those whose loved ones had come to this strange place to pick among the blackening bloated bodies. For months to come and, to a degree, throughout the great struggle, the family carriage became a symbol of both hope and dispair.

In March 1862, the Federal Napoleon, General George B. McClellan, decided to end the war for once and for all by a gigantic side-door attack on Richmond via the soupy peninsula between the York and James Rivers. Men and equipment were funneled onto the tip of this inhospitable corridor in numbers which compare favorably with the great landings of World War II, and had not McClellan suffered from, as Lincoln said, the "slows," the war indeed might have been brought to a close. As it happened, General Lee was given the time to formulate a plan of defense and attack that still sparkles in the annals of military history.

The real fighting started at Fair Oaks on May 31, 1862, and almost without letup pushed on until July 1st at Malvern Hill, the last battle of the so-called Seven Days' engagement. Here the twelve-pounder howitzers came into their own. Lined up hub to hub, they blasted the waves of screaming southerners with canister at point-blank range. Fiery hunks of metal defaced, decapitated, and eviscerated the men in butternut, and hot sulfurous smoke ate into raw wounds. All of this was pay for being pushed back to the banks of the James—and to Washington.

The Federals did not break and run—and this *was* progress. Unfortunately there had not been a similar spirit of accomplishment in the Medical Department. Although Surgeon Charles S. Tripler, Medical Director of the Army of the Potomac, had some good ideas, the medical situation turned out to be another fiasco. There were over 8,000 Federals to care for and hardly anything with which to care for them. Ambulances were almost nonexistent, one sector reported only about one for every 300 men. Tents, food, and medical supplies—what there were— seemed to have been allocated to the wrong places, thanks to the equally delinquent Quartermaster Corps. There were no doctors to speak of—one to about 1,000 men, would be a good guess—and the supposed stretcher-bearers were content to leave the wounded by the side of the road or at disinterested farmhouses. The field hospitals were still at the regimental level and staffed by medics and stewards who, as before, refused to attend to anybody but "their own."

The finale to this sort of terror came when the mangled and sick were dropped off at Harrison's Landing for ship transport to Washington. Many wagons and flatcars arrived at the landing with their human cargoes packed spoon-fashion on the floor, some having spent three or four harrowing days without a mouthful of food. In conformity with its abominable conduct on the field, the Quartermaster Corps had gathered together nothing but a lot of filthy vessels pathetically equipped and supplied. The picture by now was so desperate that the Sanitary Commission rushed to the scene and literally took over. This was going to be the first of many such times when the commission would extract the victim, still alive, from the lion's mouth.

Meanwhile, the groundwork was being laid for the Second Bull Run. Once again Lee, Longstreet, and Jackson would combine their genius to blast those Federals as they had never been blasted before. Everything was made to order, for none other than Major General John Pope was at the helm, a man who understood the battlefield in the same way Surgeon General Finley understood medicine. The fight started on August 29th and lasted until late the next day, with Pope's great Army of Virginia in complete rout and defeat.

Words do little to convey the aftermath. With a Federal casualty list of somewhere around 15,000 (Confederate, 8,400), the medical situation was just this side of pure hopelessness. Indeed, the First Bull Run was a mere twitch, while the second was a convulsion. The bulk of the supplies, including thousands of cases of chloroform, had been captured by Stonewall Jackson's men two days earlier and, as before, the teamsters hired by the quartermaster to drive the ambulance had fled the field at the first clash of battle. That Surgeon McParlin, Pope's Medical Director, proved no more competent than the general, is attested to in that instead of establishing a system of brigade and division hospitals at reasonable distances from the battlefield, he set up a single unwieldy treatment station almost ten miles away from the front lines. With the bulk of the ambulances gone and stretcher-bearers either hiding or running away, thousands of wounded and maimed lay where they fell. As night came to this littered field and the groans and screams broke the stillness of the dark, the whole thing became as ghostly as it was ghastly. For days the injured lay amid the fearful stench of putrifying cadavers, the sun's scorching rays, and drenching downpours of rain.

Desperation and chaos gripped Washington as the dazed and crippled Federals began to swell its streets and buildings. A frantic call was put out for civilian assistance to retrieve the dying and dead strewn along the little stream. Anything on wheels was commandeered and headed south, and what a sight it was— an endless caravan of hacks, wagons, carriages, and carts bouncing along the dusty trail to the bloody Run. Actually, the gesture could have really helped if a good share of the drivers had not been good-for-nothing bums who broke into the supplies, drank the liquor (the Rebellion's wonder drug) and headed back to the capital. And the few who did reach the field operated at even lower levels. They piled their vehicles high with loot and robbed the dead and the dying, the upshot being that hundreds of the tortured victims were not removed from the battlefield for a week or more.

But this was not all, for in the Western theater during the early years the conditions, though better on occasion, generally mirrored the organizational failure of the Army of the Potomac. At the small but brisk fight at Wilson's Creek (August 10, 1861), the ambulance shortage caused some of the wounded to lie on the field for a week without food or medical attention. And what happened at Perryville (October 10, 1862) seriously rivals the Bull Run spectacles. There Union commander General Don Carlos Buell's anti-medicine attitude was compounded by the exigencies of battle. Confederate General Braxton Bragg, slipping the leash, had headed straight up through Kentucky and in haste to cut him off before he reached the Ohio River, Buell saw little need to drag along such extra baggage as hospital tents and medical supplies. The 2,900 Federal wounded walked, crawled or, if lucky, were carted to the Perryville homes and the barns and farmhouses surrounding this terror-stricken town. Many stayed here for weeks without proper food or medical attention. A once happy and contented village, Perryville now suddenly became the shadowy crossroads of fever, putrid gangrene, and rigor mortis.

This, then, is a glimpse of the sorbid medical picture which prevailed in the North throughout much of the first years of the Civil War. Obviously, it could not and did not continue for the duration, the public in general and women in particular would not stand for it, especially since this war was taking place in the housewives' front yard. True, the greatest of the battles and the bulk of the carnage was yet to come, but the latter would be largely the fault of minies and canister rather than stupidity and incompetence. In point of fact, the machinery of public indignation was manifest at the very beginning in a number of small but nevertheless significant instances. Indeed, the one great spark of reform appeared only a few days following the death of Private Hough.

That spark was struck, supposedly, on a New York City street by the chance meeting of the Reverend Henry W. Bellows, a Unitarian minister, and a physician by the name of Elisha Harris. The two men visualized the horrors of the battles to come and vowed to direct their energy and talent to the treatment and prevention of human suffering. Together with a group of high-spirited New York ladies, a meeting was held at Cooper Union which resulted in the formation of the Women's Central Association of Relief for the Sick and Wounded of the Army. On May 16, 1861, delegates of this organization and other bodies of similar persuasion descended upon the War Department and demanded the formation of a Sanitary Commission.

Secretary of War Cameron, the Medical Department, and even President Lincoln himself at first took offense at this intrusion, proclaiming without reservation Washington's ability to run the war by itself. But fortunately, Surgeon General Lawson was at home sick abed and Surgeon Robert Wood was in charge. Wood could see the logic of the delegates' proposal and did much to enlighten Cameron and Lincoln on the subject. Finally realizing the American people would not stand for a Crimean-styled rebellion, Cameron approved the order creating the commission and signed it on June 9, 1861. The President approved and signed the order four days later.

Although in theory the United States Sanitary Commission was simply intended to investigate and advise on matters of "sanitary and hygienic interest," in practice it brought about a purging and cleansing of the Medical Department. Under the able direction of Frederick Law Olmsted, as Executive Secretary, the Commission throughout the war kept a close eye on camps, hospitals, food, clothing, medical supplies, ambulance service, and recruitment. Negligence and incompetence were exposed in no uncertain terms and remedial measures were suggested. To prove it practiced what it preached, the Sanitary Commission— along with other spirited organizations such as the Christian Commission—sent its workers into the field and hospitals to nurse and nourish. Right up to the end, its wagons, filled with everything from chloroform to chewing tobacco, rode the troubled trails of war. And through its famous "homes," the Commission fed and sheltered recruits, soldiers on leave, and the disabled. By war's end it had distributed approximately fifteen million dollars worth of supplies, a staggering figure for the time, particularly in that it came solely from the people. In no other war involving Americans would it be necessary for those back home—North or South—to match an ounce of blood with gallons of sweat.

Probably the most significant act performed by the Sanitary Commission was its "white paper" of September, 1861, requesting the removal of Surgeon General Finley and other corrective measures. With the assistance of heated public sentiment, a Reorganization Bill was finally passed the following April. In addition to a Surgeon General and Assistant Surgeon General, the bill provided for a Sanitary Inspector General and several Sanitary Inspectors. But the best news was the appointment of William A. Hammond as Surgeon General.

Surgeon General Hammond had vision, intelligence, ability, and unbound energy, and like all leaders of this caliber, struck out at once at the underlying trouble spots. One of his first moves was an order directing proper records for the sick, wounded, and dead. That such records had never been kept with any degree of accuracy, attests to the state of affairs when this man took over. Hammond introduced a meaningful system for the classification of disease, wrote and edited manuals relating to hygiene and sanitation, speeded up the procurement and allocation of supplies and equipment, and strove constantly to improve the quality of medical care. In addition to these rather immediate measures, the Surgeon General recommended the establishment of a permanent General Hospital in Washington, an Ambulance Corps, Army Medical Museum, and Army Medical School. Further, he proposed that the men who ran the ambulances and nursed the sick and wounded should be enlisted in and trained by the Medical Department—in short they should be true medics. Though Hammond was not around to see it, the bulk of these recommendations, in one form or other, were gradually accepted during the course of the war.

The Surgeon General's appointment of Jonathan Letterman as Medical Director of the Army of the Potomac (June, 1862) was perhaps his most significant contribution to the Cause. Letterman had great ability and so improved the medical service of the Army of the Potomac that his organization, later enacted into law, formed the basis of our present-day "field medicine." At Antietam, the bloodiest battle of the war, Letterman's ambulance system outstandingly proved its worth in that all wounded were collected and placed under shelter within twenty-four hours! Foggy heads at the top, nevertheless, restricted Letterman's ambulance and medical system to the Army of the Potomac until 1864, when the Congress was forced to create an Ambulance Corps for the entire army.

Unfortunately, Hammond's brilliance and ability were not always to his advantage in dealing with people. He was often brusk and, in the eyes of many, uncompromising and arrogant. This coupled with the fact that he had been appointed to the job over heads of those with seniority produced a good number of hierarchy enemies, not the least of whom was Secretary of War Edwin Stanton. And even so, the Surgeon General would no doubt have made it through the war had it not been for his May, 1863 "Circular No. 6," a pronunciamento which opposed the wholesale use of calomel (a cathartic) and tartar emetic (an expectorant and emetic). Taking away such revered "poisons" at this time was downright heresy, and the doctors would not stand for it. They not only flagrantly disregarded the circular, but took their gripe to Washington where it was received with open arms. The following November synthetic charges relating to liquor contracts were brought against Hammond while he was conveniently away on business. As a consequence of the Surgeon General's demand for satisfaction, a kangaroo trial was held where he was formally charged and found guilty of 'conduct unbecoming an officer and gentleman." He was dismissed from the service in August 1864. A dozen years after the war, the case was reviewed and the force of justice restored Hammond, by then an outstanding neurosurgeon, to the rank of brigadier general.

Hammond's job went to Joseph K. Barnes, not by coincidence a close friend of Secretary Stanton. Surgeon General Barnes had few gifts of special merit himself, but was smart enough to appreciate that he had inherited a worthwhile department with excellent potentialities. Indeed, under the Barnes administration the majority of recommendations and ideas set forth by Hammond became not only respectable, but acceptable.

The Confederate hayfoot-strawfoot medical situation was perhaps more desperate and demoralizing, if this were possible, due to an ever-dwindling supply of food, drugs, ambulances, tents, and the like, and had it not been for the brilliant leadership of Surgeon General Samuel Preston Moore, the consequences would have been too much to contemplate. Good or bad, the Union forces at least had a medical service to start with, whereas Moore had nothing but the confidence of Jefferson Davis and fifty or so doctors who, along with the Surgeon General, had defected from the Federal army.

Doctor Moore, a graduate of the Medical College of South Carolina, was much like his Union counterpart, Surgeon General Hammond—bright, brusque, demanding, and, above all, a capable administrator who had the respect, if not always the love, of everyone. Under the stress of overwhelming difficulties, he not only put together a medical service comparable to that of the North, but also distinguished himself, as did Hammond, in peripheral as well as strictly medical matters. Surgeon General Moore stimulated the publication and distribution of journals, manuals, and textbooks (e.g., *A Manual of Military Surgery*); founded the "Association of Army and Navy Surgeons of the Confederacy;" pioneered in certain methods of pharmacy; and popularized the use of one-story hospital wards, a development now considered a major contribution. Moore also showed foresight in the selection of the very able William Spotswood to head the surgeons of the navy.

In one important detail, interestingly enough, the respective medical services differed, and that was in the absence in the Confederacy of anything approaching the stature of the United States Sanitary Commission. Yet, the southern medical service managed to survive the terrible pressures of the day without such "outside" assistance, and this seems to underscore its workability. However, this is not to say the civilian population in the Confederate States of America were any less active. On the contrary, the country was being invaded and everybody would work and suffer. The womenfolk and those too young or too old for military service helped in any way they could, and such organizations as the Women's Relief Society, Association for Relief of Maimed Soldiers, and Ladies' Soldiers Relief Society collected money, food, and clothing and did anything else to aid the sick and wounded in this sad and troubled land.

CHAPTER III

The Doctors

THE man of medicine who served in the Civil War was, whether he liked it or not, first and foremost a "surgeon" and always referred to as such. Though his first knife may well have been government issued, he learned the tricks of the trade in due course and sometimes became quite an expert, particularly if ambidexterous. Do your best was the general idea, and most surgeons did or at least tried.

Nearly all the older doctors of the period had received their medical education on an apprenticeship basis but the younger men—those who were to make up the bulk of the army surgeons— usually held a medical school diploma of sorts in addition to an office internship. A course at a better institution might cover two years, but in the diploma mills a man could finish in a matter of weeks. Slight attention was paid to clinical instruction, and the laboratory in most instances was all but forgotten. Harvard University, for example, reportedly did not procure a microscope until after the war. Add to this the fact that many states prohibited any kind of dissection. Further, whereas stethoscopes, thermometers, syringes, ophthalmoscopes, laryngoscopes, and the like were used widely in Europe, many doctors here at home had never seen them let alone used them.

In regard to ability and competence, there is no reason to believe the doctors in the North and the South differed from each other in any significant way. Indeed, most Confederate medicos were trained in the North at such schools as the University of Pennsylvania, University of New York, Jefferson Medical

Figure 3. Dr. Jonathan Letterman, Medical Director of the Army of the Potomac *(fourth from left),* and his staff. (Library of Congress.)

College, and Harvard School of Medicine. However, the South was learning to become less dependent on the North in this area and at the outbreak of war, a number of schools had already been established. The Medical College of South Carolina was founded in 1824, and by the 1830's there were medical schools at Richmond, New Orleans, and Augusta.

Good, bad or indifferent the doctors were needed and just about every device was tried to keep up the supply, a task compounded by frequent absenteeism. One medical director, for example, reported that at a given time one-half of his staff was away. (This situation was by no means peculiar to the medical people, for many others in the Civil War had the habit of picking up their blankets and heading back to the old homestead.) Moreover, even when the staffs were in full strength they were commonly overwhelmed by the endless lines of men waiting

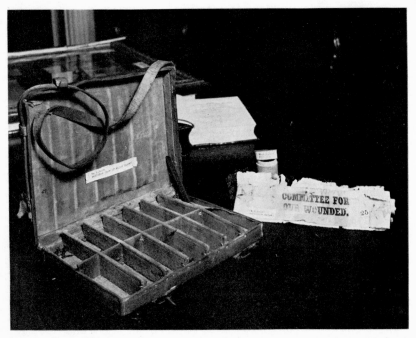

Figure 4. Confederate medicine case, hospital badge, pill box and book *(Resources of the Southern Fields and Forests, a Medical Botany of the Confederate States, Charleston, 1863).* (Confederate Museum, Richmond, Va.)

to have an arm or leg taken off. And to add insult to injury the medical schools in the South, with the exception of the University of Virginia, closed their doors. Why this was allowed to happen is still difficult to understand inasmuch as these institutions could have been used to train bright young men in the art and science of military medicine—certainly there was enough *raw material.*

At the start of the fighting, the Union had a hundred or so "regulars," that is, Surgeons and Assistant Surgeons of the United States Army, headed by the Surgeon General. These doctors filled the staff positions and formed the nucleus about which the President, Secretary of War, and Surgeon General—aided in no small measure by the Sanitary Commission—fashioned a Medical Department of some stature by 1865. This was no mean feat considering that medical men were exempt from the draft. In addition to the regulars, there were, among others, the Surgeons and Assistant Surgeons of Volunteers, Regimental Surgeons and Assistant Surgeons, Acting Assistant Surgeons of the United States Army, and "Reserve Surgeons." By the end of the war some 13,000 doctors had served in the field and in the hospitals. Full surgeons, with commission, held the rank of major and drew the substantial pay of $169.00 per month, and assistant surgeons held the rank of captain or first lieutenant and drew $115.50 and $105.50 per month, respectively.

The bulk of the doctors were regimental surgeons, that is, medical men commissioned by the governors (rather than the President) who accompanied the state regiments into battle. Eventually, the standard procedure was to provide one surgeon and two assistant surgeons per regiment, and the various states were held responsible for so doing. The manner in which these men were selected ranged from no examination at all to such "rigorous" requirements as proper credentials—namely, a diploma —and an examination prepared and supervised by specially appointed medical boards. Although the performance of the regimental medico was not infrequently questioned, the watchdog Sanitary Commission was fairly well satisfied that, in the main, the states were doing an acceptable job. Be that as it may, it was the regimental surgeon and his assistants who did just about all the sawing and cutting.

The cream of the regimental surgeons, if they so desired, took a special examination and became the somewhat select Surgeons and Assistant Surgeons of Volunteers. Placed on a par with the regulars by virtue of their presidential commission, these men were assigned to staff positions in the upper echelons and by the end of the war held the bulk of the medical directorships at the army (brevet colonel) and corps (brevet lieutenant colonel) levels.

The Acting Assistant Surgeons of the United States Army and Reserve Surgeons performed their services in more or less a twilight capacity inasmuch as they were not commissioned. The former category, known at the time as "contract surgeons," numbered somewhere around 5,500 men. Though these doctors divided their time between the general hospitals and private practice, they were given the full pay of a first lieutenant. With regard to the Reserve Surgeons, no one can tell just exactly how many served because these men were essentially free lancers. Some were undoubtedly conscientious and helpful, but most came to the battlefield and hospitals to see the sights or test their mettle at cutting and carving.

In about a year's time, the Union had forged the diverse groups into a workable system, the chain of command running from the top man in Washington, the Surgeon General, down through the Medical Directors of the army, corps, division, and brigade, in that order. In addition, and central to success, were sixteen Medical Inspectors in the field who apprised the head office—via the Medical Inspector General—of all-round performance. In this fashion, shortcomings were brought to light and remedial measures instituted whenever possible.

The Medical Department of the Confederate States of America, for all practical purposes, was a rubber stamp of the organization just described—from the Surgeon General down to the contract surgeon. The pay structure, too, was modeled after that of the United States Army, and although inflation reduced the actual value of a Southerner's military pay, this was somewhat counterbalanced by the more liberal promotion policies in the South. Some 3,500 medical officers are known to have served by 1865, including a hundred or so assigned to the navy. Notwithstanding the frightful shortage of equipment and supplies, the Confederate medical service performed as well as its Northern counterpart and perhaps on occasion demonstrated better judgment, particularly in the more serious use of medical boards to examine prospective surgeons for the regular and provisional army. Of some interest, too, the Southern service recognized dentistry as a "separate" entity and encouraged its growth in the overall medical picture, a development traceable in no small way to the unsuccessful efforts of Jefferson Davis to establish a dental corps when he was Secretary of War of the *United* States.

As to the type of man who wielded the saw and knife and dispensed the ipecac, there were, to put it mildly, mixed feelings. Civilian and soldier alike sometimes cried, "Butcher!" and when they did the newspapers could be relied upon to give a helping hand. Character attacks were common. According to a Confederate nurse, " . . . They (the doctors) drink up most of the brandy and whiskey in stock and being fired up most of the day display a cruel and brutal indifference to the needs of the suffering which is a disgrace to their profession and humanity . . . " But certainly this strong language could not have applied to the medical services at large. Perhaps Walt Whitman presented a more accurate picture when he observed, "All but a few are excellent men . . . "

Among these "excellent men" were some who contributed a great deal to American medicine. In the Confederacy, for example, Samuel Moore envisioned the hospital of the future; John Chisolm pioneered in anesthesia and military surgery; and Joseph Jones became a one-man institution of Civil War medical history in the South. Indeed, Jones' post-war writings—*Observations upon the Losses of the Confederate Armies from Wounds and Disease, The Surgical Memoirs of the War of the Rebellion,* and so on— did much to fill in the historical blanks left by the great Richmond fire.

In the Union, William Hammond and Jonathan Letterman put together the framework of a medical corps which would serve the wars of the future; Silas Mitchell became a world authority on nervous disorders; Elisha Harris founded the American Public Health Association; William Keen received international honors for his brilliant surgery; and John Billings designed Johns Hopkins Hospital and was largely responsible for the erection of the New York Public Library as it now stands. It was Keen interestingly enough, who, under great secrecy, successfully removed a cancer from the mouth of President Cleveland. Medical scholars especially will appreciate that Doctor Billings fathered the *Index Medicus,* an indispensable guide to the literature of present-day medicine.

There was also a most "excellent" woman, Mary Edwards Walker of Oswego, New York. An 1855 graduate of Syracuse Medical College, Doctor Walker entered the Union army at the beginning of the war, serving the first three years as a nurse and the last year as an *assistant surgeon*—making her the first woman in the history of the United States to hold such a commission. A nonconformist in no uncertain way (she always wore male attire), after the war this particular surgeon in blue devoted her life to the cause of equal rights and suffrage for women.

CHAPTER IV

Avalanche!

ALTHOUGH medicine in the field generally improved as the war went along, it was far from ever becoming what might be called a top priority item. In most battle situations it was usually only the officer who really could count on being well-served. As one Confederate put it, "The very woods seemed to moan and groan with the voices of sufferers not brought in ..." Nonetheless, the Rebellion's field relief by far outshone the performance in earlier wars and indeed became a model for armies of the future. Perhaps above all, there was a measure of compassion for the enemy. In the words of Major General Lew Wallace, the man who penned *Ben Hur,* "In the relief given there was no distinction between friend and foe (and) the surgeons never rested ... "

During the early battles, the field hospital, particularly among the Union forces, was chiefly of the regimental type, a setup fraught with inefficiency, bungling, and confusion. Since the regimental surgeons often refused to look after the wounded of any outfit other than their own, it was not uncommon for one hospital to be overwhelmed while the doctors just across the way were sitting around waiting for business. By the same token, unless a man happened to be shot in the vicinity of his regiment's infirmary, there was an excellent chance he would have a good long wait before being attended to. Further, the regimental system worsened the supply problem—if this were possible—through duplication and waste.

With regard to the care the patient received once he reached

Figure 5. Confederate wounded at Smith barn, Antietam, Md., with Union Doctor Anson Hurd in attendance. (Library of Congress.)

one of these places, there always remained ample ground for improvement. As mentioned earlier, the nurses were generally skulkers, shirkers, and other misfits whom the regimental commander was usually more than happy to send over to the hospitals. Often the only available nurses were convalescent soldiers, poor souls who should have been in bed themselves. At Shiloh, when the men detailed to the regimental hospitals had to be returned to the line, Federal surgeons were forced to depend upon deserters.

More often than not the field hospitals were filthy. Clara Barton noted one man whose socks had not been removed for over a month: "His toes were matted and grown together and are now dropping off at the joint; the cavities in his back are absolutely frightful . . . " So it went.

Among the Federals, field relief was dominated by the regimental setup during much of the first part of the war and was

Figure 6. A Federal field hospital at Gettysburg. (From the Gettysburg cyclorama, Gettysburg National Park.)

tainted by it throughout the war. Soon common sense prevailed and gradually the regimental hospitals were merged into the brigade hospitals and the latter, chiefly through the efforts of Medical Director Letterman, into divisional hospitals. In the Army of the Potomac, the division hospital, by the end of 1862, was the rule, and by 1863 these in turn were brought together on a corps basis. The overall effect was a better use of available supplies and, above all, surgical talent. In a word, chaos had given way to some sort of order.

The usual divisional organization in both medical services went something like this: The Surgeon-in-Chief of the division selected a regimental surgeon to head the hospital and two assistants to carry out his orders. One assistant supervised the pitching of tents, providing of straw, fuel, water, and so on, and had direct charge of the hospital stewards and nurses. It was the other assistant's job to record the patient's name, rank, company, regiment, nature of wound, and treatment. From the entire division three surgeons were selected to do all important operations or at least be responsible for them. Three others were detailed to assist. The remaining medical officers of the division, except one who stayed with the regiment, were required to act as dressers of wounds and assistants, generally. The doctor who was with the regiment was required to give first aid.

Most division hospitals, or "infirmaries" as the Confederates liked to call them, were supposed to serve, on paper at least, the medical needs of 7,000-8,000 men which meant, even by the standards then, an alarming supply problem. In the better equipped outfits, this amounted to about twenty or so wagons filled to the brim with tents, supplies, and equipment. Among the Confederate forces, however, this was a figure rarely attained, not only because of a shortage of wagons, but also of animals to pull them. In the South especially, poor transportation proved to be a major stumbling block in the development of a sound system of field medicine.

More often than not there was a shocking disparity in

Figure 7. Union field hospital at Brandy Station, Va. (Library of Congress.)

equipment and supplies. Whereas the Federal Medical Service was coming into an affluence of sorts as the Rebellion groaned on, the situation among the Confederates continued to worsen. A spot check of the hospital stores carried by the Army of the Potomac just before crossing the Rapidan in May, 1864, for instance, disclosed all kinds of medicines, dressings, and drugs and such *delicacies* as cereals, nutmeg, sugar, tea, condensed milk, canned peaches, corn starch, lemons, dried fruits, and jellies. Such items as these could win the war—and the South knew it.

During actual battle there was little difference in approach between the medics in blue and gray. The first piece of business was setting up the field hospital, which as we have seen ranged in size from the pigsty regimental infirmary to the large, fairly well-managed brigade, division, and corps installations. Buildings were used when available—mills, churches, schools, farmhouses,

Figure 8. Ambulance wagons and drivers at Washington's Harewood Hospital. (Library of Congress.)

cow barns, to name a few—but more often than not these had to be supplemented with canvas. The one big consideration was distance to the main line of fighting. To wit: situate close, but not too close, at that time a stretch of somewhere between one and one-half to two miles—just beyond shell range.

The regimental commanders would then assign between thirty and forty men—usually including the band—as nurses and litter-bearers, the nurses reporting to the field hospital to help the surgeons and hospital stewards ready the supplies and equipment, while the stretchermen accompanied the assistant surgeons and their orderlies to a forward first aid, or "primary," station. If all went well, the forward stations could boast of pails, basins, sponges, lint, bandages, splints, tourniquets, chloroform, opium, morphine, and a fair amount of whiskey. All forward medics were unarmed and wore badges to distinguish themselves from the rest of the command. Each carried a canteen of water, a tin cup, and a knapsack containing first aid supplies and, usually, a pint or so of whiskey. "Under no circumstances" were regular line troops permitted to break rank and give a hand. To do so in most commands meant severe punishment.

Slightly wounded men had to walk to the primary stations, while the badly injured were at the mercy of the unpredictable stretchermen. Treatment was with rare exception confined to checking hemorrhage, bandaging wounds, and administering opiates for pain and whiskey to counter shock. (Though perhaps contrary to the teachings of modern medicine, few questioned the efficacy of using whiskey in shock a hundred years ago.) The wounded unable to walk were loaded into ambulances for a bouncy, bumpy ride of a mile or so to the field hospital where, upon arrival, they were lifted onto the operating table for "detailed" examination. If an operation—almost always an amputation—was necessary it was done then and there. How long a man would stay at this location depended very much on the fighting. In the event things were quiet and the army did not move, he might remain there long enough to recover—or die. In most instances, however, the patients were evacuated within a few days to a base hospital sometimes as far away as Baltimore or Richmond.

This brings up the matter of transportation, for in field relief all else has little meaning without some sort of system for getting the wounded to the depots and base hospitals. Although the Federal medical service eventually emerged with a model setup, during the first year of the fighting there was not too much difference in the performance of the respective "Ambulance Corps."

The two Bull Run engagements, as we have seen, could not have been worse for the Union. Not only were the ambulances too few, too far between, and too late, but also, and worse yet, driven by civilian drunks and thieves who started to run when the Napoleons began to roar. To add insult to injury someone in the Quartermaster Corps—the outfit responsible for the mess—had decided to use two-wheeled ambulances on the theory that they were "better suited for the seriously wounded." A ride in one of those insolent chariots on a corduroy road must have been a kind of vehicular purgatory even to one in the best of health. Actually, not a few of the wounded were jarred to death, and overnight the two-wheeler became known throughout the Army of the Potomac as the "avalanche."

By an act of God, the avalanche soon left the scene, not so much because of the torture involved, but because it was always on the blink. During the first year, just about all had undergone repair and a good half of them had been scrapped. Though their four-wheeler successors left much to be desired, it was at least a gesture in a forward direction—and how this war needed such gestures!

Upon the appointment of Jonathan Letterman as Medical Director of the Army of the Potomac, the Union ambulance system took a decided turn for the better. Letterman's ability and enthusiasm made a fast impression on McClellan, with the result that the general gave him a blank check to improve the care of the sick and wounded. Here it must be said that although McClellan had the "slows" in battle, he acted with speed when it came to organization and efficiency. And too, he loved his men, and they loved him.

Letterman took the ambulances away from the Quartermaster Corps and placed them on a corps basis with himself in charge. A captain headed the corps, a first lieutenant the division, a second lieutenant the brigade, and a sergeant the regiment. Gradually this system in one form or another seeped into other commands and armies, and by 1864 Congress had created an Ambulance Corps for the entire Union forces. When available this amounted to about four ambulances per regiment manned by "specially trained" drivers.

Among the Confederate forces the ambulance system was poor from the start, and toward the end of the war just about hopeless. The medical people did well with what they had, but were plagued by a terrible lack of both wagons and animals. According to the surgeons in high places, this proved to be the most serious medical problem in the South. In the beginning they too had their avalanche chariots—two per regiment (on paper, that is to say).

The ambulances and wagons, however, would have amounted to just about naught had it not been for the railroads. Although the railroad hospital train was often an unheated cattle car bedded with straw, particularly in the South, sometimes the wounded man encountered spic and span passenger coaches specially equipped with beds, kitchens, dispensaries, and surgeries. By the fall of 1862, regular daily hospital train service was in effect between Washington and New York, and by the end of the conflict Northern railroads had carried 225,000 sick and wounded from the field to the general hospitals.

In the South the railroads were "relatively good" and the chief mode of transporting patients from the front lines to the interior. But, a train ride was more often than not a harrowing experience. Commonly, the cars were unheated and without water and were jerked mercilessly along by inconsiderate engineers. Frequent delays and jumping the track were routine; five days after the battle of Chickamauga twenty carloads of desperately sick Southerners were still waiting to be pulled along.

Upon the coastal waters and Western rivers were the Union hospital ships, a luxury not to be enjoyed to any significant degree by the Southern forces. Some vessels were nothing more than dirty freighters, but in time there appeared a good number of well-groomed steamers, ingeniously adapted for the transportation of sickly men. The City of Memphis, for example, carried 7,000 casualties from the battle site at Fort Henry to hospitals along the Ohio River. In the beginning, these ships were run by the Quartermaster Corps and later on, when it became obvious the Corps was more interested in nonhuman cargoes, by the Medical Department and Sanitary Commission.

The first *naval* hospital ship was the Red Rover, a Mississippi side wheeler captured from the Confederates when Island Number 10 fell in April, 1862. Commanded by the very able Surgeon Ninian Pinkney, the vessel had clean beds, elevators between decks, a well-equipped operating room, and even screened windows—earning for itself the complimentary sobriquet of "floating palace." Perhaps the Red Rover's principal claim to fame was that it reportedly carried the first female nurses of the navy.

It must be squarely appreciated that the aforementioned approach to medicine in the field was not by any means what might be called "standard procedure." Things in the War Between the States did not work that way. Usually what emerged amidst the smoke and metal was a little of this and a little of that, an axiom epitomized by a good look at any of the really big battles.

Take the situation at Shiloh, by way of illustration. As the Federals were being driven toward the river the brigade field hospitals and ambulance systems were shattered to pieces. The nurses were ordered back to the ranks—those who were not running for dear life—and the only people the surgeons and stewards could collar to succor the wounded men were the deserters headed for the river. Medical supplies and equipment were blown to the wind, and without a doubt the only serious bandaging on the first day was carried out by a handful of female nurses who were using grass, leaves, and torn shirts. Nevertheless, out of this mess a Surgeon Irwin succeeded in putting together from commandeered infantry tents a field hospital holding some 2,500 men, an effort which yielded to military medicine its first hospital entirely under canvas. Thus, field relief started badly but ended well that horrible spring day. But yet this was not always the case. At the First and Second Bull Runs, the wounded lay among the dead for days; at Perryville, General Buell decided to leave behind his medical impedimenta; at Fredericksburg shattered bodies wallowed in bloody warehouse molasses; at Gettysburg, Lee came away with a seventeen-mile-long springless caravan of unattended, maimed men. And so on . . .

In the wake of tremendous slaughter, even the best was pathetically little. When Lee and McClellan clashed along Antietam Creek the water under Burnside's Bridge actually ran red, and at the end of that bloodiest day in American history there were 10,000 Federals and 4,500 Confederates crying for help. To this staggering number of tortured men can be added another 3,000 at nearby Frederick, Maryland, who had been cut down three days before at South Mountain.

The medical situation at Gettysburg was as overpowering as was the unbearable stench emanating from the 10,000 dead soldiers and 3,000 dead horses about the area. Just exactly what happens when a sleepy little town of 2,500 people is suddenly presented with 22,000 desperately sick men? A Union medical officer's remark that the aftermath was an "occasion of the greatest amount of human suffering known to this nation since its birth" still holds true, despite a lapse of a century and two great wars. The wounded lay on the field, under trees, beside the road, and in farmhouses, barns, churches, and haystacks for miles around. Since the Federals had pushed on in pursuit of Lee, only a fraction of the medical people were left behind to mend the flesh, let alone bury the dead. For a good week after the battle, wagons and ambulances were still going over the fields collecting dying men. This was the sleepy little town that had a sign posted reading: "Anyone shooting a gun within the graveyard will be subject to a $5 fine!"

The first order of business at Gettysburg and the other great battles entailed sorting out those who could be saved from those who could not, a chore Civil War medicine handled with considerable dispatch. For instance, a man shot in the head or spine was beyond help and that was that. Such wounded were merely placed in orderly rows and left to the resources of nature. In the fields about the town of Gettysburg that hot and sultry fourth of July were hundreds of semiconscious Yanks and Confederates moaning and groaning and twitching—and all alone. But for the others there was Yankee ingenuity and hope. Every house and barn became a primary station, and even the churches were tailored to the Cause by the placing of planks across the pews for beds. And in a couple of days an immense tent hospital was established in the low ground behind Cemetery Ridge, just across the way from George Pickett's frantic last charge. The cry for help caught fire throughout the land and soon trains and wagons of mercy were descending upon the gasping crossroads. In a week's time America's greatest horror had given way to a relatively neat, well-managed city of shattered bones and healing stumps.

But medicine in the field was by no means restricted to minies and canister, for *surgeon's call* was held daily, usually right after reveille. This was the time for the sick—and the pretenders —to file past the regimental surgeon and hear the verdict on their signs and symptoms, real or otherwise. If a man had a good color, a healthy tongue, and normal bowels his chances of getting off duty were usually slim. But seldom did he come away empty handed, especially if the outfit had a well-stocked medicine wagon. A dose of calomel for "tightness" or a dose of opium for "looseness" would do the trick.

CHAPTER V

Pails and Pavilions

Everybody saw the great war coming and yet somehow it seemed everybody thought it would turn about and eventually go away. Perhaps this is why the people above and below the Mason-Dixon line were not overly concerned with hospitals and the like. Besides, hospitals were dirty, smelly, and contaminated, and, according to the man on the street, a good place to stay out of—especially when sick. Even after the fighting was well under way who but Medical Director Tripler of the Army of the Potomac should look upon general hospitals as "general nuisances." Abroad there was agreement, too, for no less an international figure than Sir John Pringle held that large hospitals were the chief cause of mortality in the army.

Be that as it may, this attitude started to change immediately after the First Bull Run and was appreciably subdued by the Second. After all, a nation can not leave its sick and mutilated warriors lying about the forests and meadows and pigsty field infirmaries to rot away just because large hospitals are unhealthy. Moreover, a good many people were beginning to have second thoughts on the matter, particularly in light of Florence Nightingale's revelations in the Crimean War. To the astonishment of the doctors, Miss Nightingale made it very clear that large hospitals were not necessarily deadly. The dictum? Throw up the windows —and use lots of soap and water.

At the outbreak of the war there was not a single general military hospital in the country, and the largest post hospital, at Fort Leavenworth, Kansas, had only forty-one beds. Thus, the

41

Figure 9. General view of Washington's Harewood Hospital showing the Capitol in the distance. (Library of Congress.)

North and South were presented with a "housing problem" of fantastic proportions. Dazed, broken bodies hobbled and crawled back to Washington and Richmond only to find no hospitals worthy of mention save a few worndown buildings of civilian origin. For a good part of 1861, and to a degree throughout the protracted struggle, anything had to do, from church pews and hotel lobbies in the towns and cities to sheds and barns out on the farms. At one stage, the Georgetown prison was emptied to provide space, and even as late as the summer of 1862 casualties were being housed in the Rotunda and Congress of the Capitol. And the people, too, were asked to open their hearts and homes to the bleeding men. Ironically, Federal wounded were housed in none other than the Lee Mansion at Arlington, Virginia.

A gigantic building program was commenced, the likes of which Americans had never seen. In the Union, William Hammond (while still an Assistant Surgeon) as early as 1861 recommended the construction of general hospitals in West Virginia, and by the spring of 1862, mainly due to his continual prodding, wooden structures were put up in that state at Parkersburg, Grafton, and Newkirk. By the end of the year, the Federal Quartermaster Corps was building all across the country, from Detroit to St. Augstine, and from New York to Jefferson, Indiana. At the begining of 1863, the Union had 151 hospitals (with 58,715 beds) , and by 1865, there were 204, with the unbelievable bed capacity of 136,894! Further, history shows that this infirmary system of the New World, which started on less than a shoestring, served not only the needs of well over one million sick and wounded soldiers, but also set the lowest mortality rate (8 per cent) of all wars theretofore.

Averaging about 500 beds apiece, the Union hospitals ranged in size from 100 or so to the huge Satterlee General at Philadelphia which could accommodate up to 3,500 men! In addition to Philadelphia, major hospital installations were located at New York; Baltimore; Chattanooga; Louisville; Memphis; Nashville; Fortress Monroe, Virginia; City Point, Virginia; Jefferson, Indiana;

Figure 10. Roper's Hospital, Charleston, S. C. (Library of Congress.)

and Washington, the nation's capital, with sixteen hospitals, having the dubious distinction of leading all other cities in bed capacity. In a very real sense Washington was, by 1864, one big meandering infirmary. The better known hospitals in the city at that sick and troubled time included Harewood, Lincoln, Stanton, Carver, Georgetown, Armory Square, Mount Pleasant, Campbell, and Judiciary Square, the latter having been visited frequently by the Lincolns. At some of these places an attempt had been made at landscaping and a few could boast of a green lawn and a flower garden or two.

Washington, incidentally, was perhaps one of the unhealthiest places in the country during this period; for superimposed on its already sticky, filthy streets and hot, fetid, malarious atmosphere was the sewage and pestilence of the hospitals and surrounding army camps. Indeed, even as late as 1881 things were bad enough to cause Garfield's doctors to order the dying President out of the city and into a more "salubrious environment."

All hospitals were not of the "general" type, the principle readily being accepted that special facilities afford certain advantages in regard to both treatment and research. This was especially true in the instance of infectious diseases where "pesthouses" were used for smallpox, eruptive fevers, and the like, the chief idea being *isolation*. At the end of the war, the Union Medical Department could point with some pride to hospitals devoted to eye and ear conditions, orthopedics, venereal diseases and nervous disorders; Philadelphia's Turner Lane Hospital acquired world reknown in the latter category.

Throughout the chaos, sorrow, and agony, the Confederacy also rose to the occasion. In the wake of the First Bull Run, wounded rebels filled the houses, sheds, and barns all the way from the little stream to Richmond, with the city iself one vast hospital. In the aftermath of Shiloh, the floors of just about every building in nearby Corinth were slippery with blood. During the Seven Days' engagement, Richmond and environs were literally over-run with festered humanity, and the mortality at the sardine-packed improvisations was alarming. Typhoid, pneumonia, mumps, and measles seemed to be everywhere, and hospital "staph" and "strep" were beginning to make their presence known.

Toward the end of 1862, however, improvement could be noted in the South, and well-developed plans for hospital organization were in the works. Increased appropriations for construction flowed from the Confederate Congress, and the War Department assumed control over all institutions housing military patients, in the process doing away with the small inefficient hospitals and infirmaries. Whether or not all this could have been successfully carried out in the absence of such a man as Surgeon General Moore is a moot question, for the problems—particularly shortages—were tremendous. Of course, Moore certainly did not do the job singlehanded. Indeed, he did have the invaluable assistance of Hospital Directors William S. Carrington, Samuel H. Stout, and James B. McCaw, men who compared most favorably with anyone in the North engaged in similar endeavors.

The Confederacy had approximately 150 general hospitals with one-third of them located in and about the city of Richmond. The most outstanding, and a medical marvel of the war, was the 8,000 bed Chimborazo, perhaps the largest hospital ever built in the world. During the course of the war, some 76,000 men were treated there. Situated on Chimborazo Heights overlooking the James River, this gigantic complex (opened early in 1862) consisted of 150 single-story pavilions organized into five "divisions," each staffed by forty to fifty assistant surgeons and headed by a surgeon-in-charge. In overall command was the able and talented James B. McCaw. (An interesting side light is that his son, Walter D. McCaw, became an outstanding military man in his own right, and toward the close of World War I was appointed Chief Surgeon of the American Expeditionary Forces in France.)

Other Richmond hospitals of note included the 5,000 bed Winder Hospital and, just outside the city, the "excellent and very clean" 2,500 bed Jackson Hospital. The thirty or so Virginia hospitals outside the Richmond area were not, generally speaking, on a par with the metropolitan institutions, some being nothing more than delapidated warehouses or factories. Next to Virginia in hospital strength ranked Georgia (with fifty hospitals), institutions in Atlanta leading the state, with the well-run Fair Grounds Hospital being typical.

In addition to the general hospitals, the Southern medical service also tried its hand at specialization, an orthopedic infirmary being put up in Richmond for the sole purpose of treating gunshot injuries and deformities. The Confederates did much in the area of dental surgery—pioneered, as it were—and often set aside a pavilion or two at a general hospital for performing surgery upon the face and mouth.

Most hospitals—Northern and Southern—were one or two story affairs constructed on the "pavilion plan;" that is, each ward, or pavilion, was detached, usually on three sides, from the main corridor. And in the "isolated plan," each pavilion was a separate building; the one story version, or "hut," is said to have been introduced by Surgeon General Moore. The over-all idea of the pavilion system, however, is generally believed to have been suggested by the British hospital design in the Crimean War.

According to specifications set forth in a Federal Army circular of July, 1864, each ward should be a ridge-ventilated pavilion, 187 feet by 24 feet and 14 feet high at the eaves, equipped with a room at one end for nurses and a room at the other end for medicines and other supplies. A ward so constructed was supposed to "accommodate sixty patients, allowing more than 1,000 cubic feet . . . " A typical Confederate hut was somewhat smaller (e.g., 100 x 30 x 12) and intended to house about fifty patients. The Federals embellished the pavilion concept in an ultra-modern fashion at Jefferson General Hospital (Jeffersonville, Indiana) where no less than twenty-four huge rectangular wards radiated out from a half mile circular corridor. Ancillary features included huge kitchens, laundries, operating rooms, pharmacies, food cellars, ice houses, and a "dead house."

As indicated, the idea of adequate ventilation was uppermost in the minds of everyone, save perhaps the inmates who looked askance at the effluvia-laden night air. In some hospitals the doctors and nurses were constantly going around opening windows while the patients were close behind shutting them. Although at this stage in American medicine the patient might on occasion know as much about medical science as the people who were treating him, here at least was one area where the doctors and nurses were on firm ground. By 1862, the mortality among the sick and wounded housed in tents and other breezy installations was significantly lower than among those held in more elaborate, but poorly ventilated infirmaries. Considering the ease and speed by which viruses and bacteria get around in contaminated areas, this startling disclosure can be readily understood and appreciated today.

The mania for fresh air worked right in with the principles of sanitation, for in Civil War medicine foul air, or noxious effluvia, meant nothing but trouble and disease. The main concern of hospitals in this regard centered on the handling of sewage and the procurement of water, problems which were considered solved when neither the air nor the water was noticeably befouled. Though there were no bacteriologists to shudder at such naiveté, history would show that the general line of reasoning made sense. Notwithstanding honest attempts to put in some kind of plumbing, the effluvia usually managed to get the upper hand and taint the hospital environment North and South. True, there were latrines and privies and sinks, and so on, but seldom was there a workable flushing system to carry the sewage far enough away to make much difference. And matters were not helped, of course, when some patients occasionally ignored the plumbing in showing preference for a nearby pail. Louisa May Alcott came to grips with the vilest odors that ever assaulted the human nose by arming herself with lavendar water: "I besprinkled myself and premises (and) like my friend, Sairy . . . was soon known among my patients as 'the nurse with the bottle'!" And how many such bottles could have been used in this war . . . !

As far as water was concerned, any source would serve the purpose just so long as it was fairly clear and above all not smelly. That it might harbor *Salmonella typhosa* or similar microbial characters was a consideration reserved for the following century. In theory, water supplies were managed by the erection of large tanks "kept supplied from wells and springs by a steam

engine," but in practice, such tanks were sometimes not to be
found, and often the water came from a nearby creek or river.
Understandably, filtration and any kind of chemical treatment
were sanitary ideas well-beyond the time. In hospitals where there
was plenty of water—an uncommon circumstance relative to present-day standards—the official suggestion was that "water-closets
may be constructed in one of the small rooms attached to each
ward, but otherwise privies are to be built at a convenient distance
and emptied at night."

The topic of water or more precisely, the lack of it, brings
up the subject of fire, one of the great enemies of the nineteenth
century. The ingredients were all there—dried out wooden buildings, naked-flame illumination, faulty stoves, rent-ridden chim-
neys, and for all practical purposes nothing but trickles of water.
Few hospitals emerged unscathed. Amid the shrieks of the sick
and wounded unable to get to their feet, flames devoured Washington's E Street Infirmary in 1861, and three years later the
Samuel Preston Moore Hospital at Griffin, Georgia went up in
smoke, with little remaining except blackened walls and smolder-
ing timbers.

CHAPTER VI

Matrons and Inmates

I NASMUCH as running a hospital can still be a harrowing experience, one can readily appreciate the goings-on in the pavilions of Civil War vintage, not a few such places coming very close indeed to meeting the specifications indicated in Dante's *Inferno*.

The typical general hospital of the Confederate States of America was headed by the Surgeon-in-Charge who in turn was immediately responsible to the Medical Director of Hospitals, the latter officer being accountable to the Surgeon General. Regular army and contract surgeons, mainly the latter, were "permanently" assigned, to each hospital at a ratio of about one doctor per seventy or so patients. Domestic matters, nursing, and general management devolved upon the matrons and assistant matrons who discharged these considerable responsibilities through a motley crew of nurses, cooks, laundresses, and innumerable other people. A wardmaster looked after the effects of the patients, furniture, cooking utensils, and the like; and the hospital steward supervised the stores, dispensed drugs, kept medical records, and saw to it that sanitary measures were enforced. Aside from the doctor, the steward was the only man in either service with any kind of training in medical matters, generally in civilian life having been a medical student or apothecary. In the Southern service he held the rank of sergeant and in the Northern service the rank of warrant officer.

The Northern hospitals were organized in more or less the same manner—from the Surgeon-in-Charge down to the attendants who stoked the fires and emptied the slop buckets. The prob-

Figure 11. Maimed soldiers and others before office of the United States Christian Commission. (Library of Congress.)

lems were about the same, not as desperate, perhaps, but always bad enough.

The situation in nursing reared its ugly head with the casualties at the First Bull Run and continued to vex the medical people in both camps to the very end, especially the men who ran the hospitals. The supply of nurses was never sufficient and before long it seemed that just about anybody who could apply a lint bandage was associated with the Cause. A fair cross-section engaged in the practice included undesirable soldiers, ("the ineffectives under arms") convalescents, invalids, prisoners, those too young or to old for military service, relatives, and recruited females. Roughly speaking, the ratio of male to female nurses in both Northern and Southern hospitals was about five-to-one.

The art and science of mid-nineteenth century nursing was just about on the same par as scrubbing floors. In most civilian hospitals—which were few, far-between, and filthy—the hapless

patient had to rely on aged inmates, prisoners, derelects or, at
best, down-and-outs who could not find a job doing anything else.
Few people worth their salt entered the "profession"—and certainly no *lady*. But things were about to change. Not only did
the early slaughters at Bull Run and the Seven Days' Battle signal
a skyrocketing demand for hospital beds, but also a realization
that the sick and mangled needed more than a whack of the saw
or a shot of whiskey. Overnight, Washington and Richmond
became forlorn cities of mutilated flesh, disease, and pestilence;
and overnight, the female nurse became a recognized angel of
mercy.

The horrors of the Crimean War (1854-1856) and the work
of Florence Nightingale were much remembered, and underscored in no uncertain way what the country had to do to amelior-
ate the agony. This war, like any war, was going to be a living
hell, but people would care—care enough, that is, to wash a putrid

Figure 12. Carver Hospital in Washington. (U. S. Signal Corps photo No.
11-B-358 [Brady Collection] National Archives.)

wound or close a dead man's eyes. The Civil War came along at a time when the female was beginning to look beyond the cookstove toward the strange and exciting world outside, and for a good many this struggle would be an excellent and honorable reason for opening the door.

Well into the nineteenth century, the only methodical attendance on the sick was done by Catholic and Protestant sisters and at the start of the fighting in 1861, they were the only *trained* nurses available North or South. The Sisters of Charity and Sisters of Mercy went immediately to the hospitals in Washington and before long, twelve religious orders were putting the teachings of Florence Nightingale into action. Otherwise, the system for supplying female nurses to the service was a hit or miss affair, particularly in the Confederacy where the women's rights movement lagged behind the North.

Female nurses of the Civil War were of all sorts and types from all walks of life. Some were relatives or good Samaritans who lived nearby; some were sent by state agencies and aid societies; and thousands were recruited through government agencies. A good many were brought into the Union hospitals through the office of Dorothea Lynde Dix who by the time of the war was a recognized leader in social reform and, more to the point, wellversed in the mechanics of the British Sanitary Commission and the work of Florence Nightingale. When she approached the Secretary of War and offered to serve—without pay—in the vital area of nurse recruitment, her services were accepted immediately. Appointed "Superintendent of Female Nurses of the Army" on April 19, 1861, Miss Dix was given the authority to recruit nurses pursuant to a special act providing that "women might be substituted for men in general or permanent hospitals."

Contrary to some histories relating to her performance, Dorothea Dix's role as superintendent left much to be desired. She was admittedly a poor administrator, quite inflexible, somewhat biased, and, as far as the doctors were concerned, too bossy. To the Surgeon-in-Charge's great consternation, Miss Dix not infrequently rubbed the hospital doctors the wrong way, especially in her apathy toward the Catholic sisters, whom the doctors considered the "perfect nurses." In a word, what they liked about the sisters was their devotion to Florence Nightingale's dictum of "silent obedience." Aside from the nuns, the doctors often resented the intrusion into their domain, especially when the "wretched females" saw fit to try out "mother's pet home remedies." According to one matron, "Many surgeons . . . were determined by a systematic course of ill-treatment toward women to drive them from the service . . . "

Notwithstanding such hostility, the chief stumbling block in Superintendent Dix's setup was in her unrealistic requirements. Among other things, ". . . The applicant must be over thirty, plain looking, dressed in brown or black . . . and no bows, no curls, no jewelry and no hoop skirts." Consequently, thousands of women were turned away from her office for such reasons as "too young," "too attractive" or "over-anxious." Further, Miss Dix's coordinating powers were interfered with appreciably as a result of War Department Order Number 351 which stated in part that, " . . . Women nurses will be assigned only on application to the General Superintendent *unless* . . . they are specifically appointed by the Surgeon General." All of which meant, of course, that surgeons not desiring to employ the Dix people could persuade the Surgeon General to make a "special appointment" of their own choosing. Although the precise figures are not known, somewhere between 3,000-4,000 women are believed to have served in Union hospitals.

Though the Confederacy did not put into motion anything quite like the superintendency described above, apparently not a great deal was lost by its failure to do so. Perhaps more realistically, it simply authorized the hospitals to hire female nurses and attendants by an Act of 1862, recommending that each ward should have two matrons, a wardmaster, and such other aides as needed—"giving preference to females." Full time people were placed under military control and paid approximately eleven dollars per month, just about the same remuneration as accorded Dorothea Dix and her nurses in the North.

The feminine touch revolutionized the care of the sick and maimed. Women proved strong morale builders and even at this singularly unsophisticated period the mental outlook of the patient was beginning to be recognized as a cardinal element in recovery. Female nurses bandaged, gave medicine, washed, cooked, read, sang, wrote letters, prayed, and wiped sweat from the brows of dying boys. One nurse wrote, "I kneel reverently by the mangled limbs of these heroes and thank God and man for the privilege of washing them." No wonder the patients preferred to be ministered to by the female rather than the male nurse.

Few actually functioned at the scene of battle or field hospitals, but occasionally an angel of mercy did appear amidst the sound and the fury—and history would never forget it. To be sure, there was Clara Barton, a self-styled bundle of energy who went on after the war to found the American Red Cross.

Clarissa Harlowe Barton was born on Christmas Day, 1821, at North Oxford, Massachusetts, the fifth and last child of Captain Stephen Barton, a discerning farmer who had fought in the Indian War alongside "Mad Anthony" Wayne. Although a timid child, Clara was restless and curious, and in adulthood became a symbol of strength and devotion. "I have learned that next to Heaven, our highest duty was to love and serve our country and honor and support its laws," she wrote. Things military fascinated her and one gets the impression that, had it not been for her sex, she would have been a candidate for West Point. Little wonder, then, that she became the first woman to share in the horrors of "modern" warfare at the scene of battle.

Dressed in a dark skirt, plaid jacket, and red bow at the neck, Clara headed straight to the front lines on the mule train, piled high with everything from splints and drugs to wine and fruit juices. Once there and often under fire she bandaged wounds, extracted minies and fed "bread sopped in wine" (her favorite concoction) to dying men. At Culpepper, at Fairfax Station, at Bull Run, at Antietam, and at Fredericksburg, this amazing woman disregarded shot and shell to do a job she knew had to be done. A Federal surgeon remembered Clara Barton as an " . . . independent Sanitary Commission of one, traveling with a prairie schooner loaded with medical supplies . . . With sleeves rolled up to the elbows, with skirt turned up . . . a lady of pleasing countenance stood beside a huge kettle hung over a roaring fire, using a ladle to stir something like a barrelful of soup, which, by frequent testing, she appeared to be seasoning to make it palatable to her hundreds of wounded heroes."

Of note too, were Mary Ann Bickerdyke and Anna Etheridge. "Mother" Bickerdyke was a Sanitary Commission worker in the West who ministered to the needs of the wounded in no less than nineteen battles. A veteran recalled that at one massacre Mother Bickerdye, in the blackness of night, moved up and down among the dead to make sure no living man should be left alone "amid such surroundings."

Anna Etheridge ("Michigan Annie," "Gentle Anna," "Our Annie," and so on) apparently did everything but fire a Napoleon. Enlisted as a nurse with the Second Michigan at the outbreak of the war, Anna served for four years under combat conditions. She was wounded in the hand at Chancellorsville, and on another occasion a soldier whose wound she was dressing was struck by a shell and literally torn apart. For her bravery throughout the war—some say her dress acquired a number of bullet holes— Anna Etheridge was awarded the Kearny Cross of the Legion of Honor.

There were Southern women in the field too. "I found the barn filled with wounded men and not one thing provided for them. They were lying about the floor on a little straw. Some had been there for two or three days and had not seen a surgeon. I washed and dressed the wounds of about fifty and poured water over the bandages of many more . . . ," wrote one Confederate nurse.

The most famous nurse in the South was Sally Louisa Tompkins, the granddaughter of Colonel John Patterson, a hero of the battle of Monmouth of the Revolutionary War. When Jefferson Davis appealed for help from the people of Richmond in the wake of the First Bull Run, Miss Tompkins secured the use of Judge John Robertson's residence and at her own expense maintained it as a hospital until 1865. Bible in hand, this frail, diminutive, and demure young lady flitted about procuring the necessary food and drugs, directing the hospital routine, and helping out the other nurses in the care of the sick and wounded. From August 1861 to April 1865, there were only seventy-three deaths out of the 1,333 admissions—an astounding feat considering the fact that the worst cases were sent there. When an executive order placed all hospitals under government control, rather than lose the Robertson Hospital Davis commissioned Sally Tompkins a *captain* in the Confederate Service, making her the South's only female officer to emerge from the war. Though she was far from what could be called a classic beauty, "Captain Sally's" character, personality, and devotion are said to have prompted many proposals of marriage.

Nursing had its literary touch, also. Louisa May Alcott's service (although brief) at Georgetown's Union Hotel Hospital prompted her to pen *Hospital Sketches,* perhaps the best account of what hospital life during at least one year of the war was really like: " . . . We dress by gaslight . . . run through the ward and throw up the windows . . . No notice is taken of our appeals for better ventilation . . . A more perfect pestilence box than this I never saw—cold, damp, dirty, full of vile odors from wounds, kitchens, and stables . . . No competent head, male or female, to right matters and indifferent nurses, surgeons and attendants to complicate the chaos still more . . . " And the most illustrious male nurse was Walt Whitman:

> " . . . I dress the perforated shoulder, the foot with
>   the bullet wound,
>   Cleanse the one with a gnawing and putrid gangrene,

so sickening, so offensive,
While the attendant stands behind me holding the
    tray and pail . . . "*

But nursing was only one facet of the hospital enigma. In the South, the lack of food proved the monster, a pathetic situation which the Northern patient did not, *relatively* speaking, have to experience. Inflation and the inability of the Confederate Subsistence Department to furnish adequate victuals (thanks in no small part to the blockade) plagued the hospitals almost from the start. The price of an egg shot up from fifteen cents in 1862 to about five dollars in 1864 and by the end of the war, watermelons were going for ten dollars apiece. The hardtack was wormy, the beef—when available—insipid, and the chicory and acorn coffee singularly vile. In the Federal states, on the other hand, many hospitals could boast of jellies, lemons, condensed milk, turkeys, chocolate, and real bread. As a matter of fact, for a time during the first year of this insane war, the bakeries situated in the vaults beneath the western terrace of the Capitol were turning out 16,000 loaves of bread daily and a little later a gigantic establishment at Fortress Monroe was putting out 30,000 loaves a day!

The hospital routine also went astray due to a lack of water, medical supplies, soap, wood, stoves, stove pipes, and ice, to name a few. Inasmuch as the feverish patient longs for something cool, it was no small morale booster that an occasional hospital could fill its icehouse. Actually, it was the scarcity of ice which caused the hospitals to shun the vitamin-charged fruits and vegetables and stock up instead on such things as tapioca, farina, beans, and salted meat.

And there were matters of sanitation and discipline. Even at best, the plumbing left much to be desired and when the men saw fit to relieve themselves at the nearest pail or bucket, the overall effect defies the imagination, particularly when compounded with gangrenous wounds, unemptied bed pans, and the effluvia

*From *The Wound Dresser.*

seeping into the wards from adjacent stables and roach-ridden kitchens. The same fellows who found it inconvenient to employ the "established" latrines frequently proved disconcertingly robust in regard to gambling, drinking, and raising cain. In the more loosely managed institutions, the convalescents who were up and about usually felt quite free to punch one another at the drop of a hat or throw tableware across the mess hall.

Unhappily, the great majority of the sick who peopled the military hospitals across the troubled land had neither the energy nor the desire for such sport. Some just wanted to die, for twisted bodies, splintered bones, raw flesh, burning fevers, and fetid air are more often than not the fabric of gloom and doom. History records, though, that in the main the doctors and the nurses did their best to alter the picture, and one has good cause to wonder just what it all would have been like if they had acted otherwise.

The big event of the day for most of the patients was the early morning visit by the ward surgeon who, with an attendant at his side, would pass from cot to cot asking questions, examining wounds, manipulating the tissues, and writing out the orders. Pinned to the shirt of each patient was a tag bearing name, rank, and unit, and at the foot of the bed were affixed cards setting forth diagnosis and treatment, and indicating whether the diet for this or that particular man was "full," "half," or "low." The full diet given routinely to convalescents covered the spectrum of the period's nutritional ideas—namely, beef, pork, beans, bread and butter, cabbage, some kind of pudding, and coffee. On occasion such items as lemons and lettuce were mentioned. The low diet was prescribed for the most desperate cases and might include rice, farina, toast, milk, and tea or cocoa. Everybody else was given the half diet which, among other things, generally consisted of some kind of soup, potatoes, bread and butter, and coffee.

Being a patient at a Civil War hospital was, even under the very best of conditions, a singularly sad and lonely business, but fortunately the country as a whole could not have agreed more. This was especially true of the folks back home, who put together every penny they could afford to buy jams and jellies and pickles for their boys so far away. The United States Christian Commission, Ladies' Aid Societies, and other groups canvassed the land high and low for donations and gifts to help fill the empty hours and brighten the long hospital day. The chaplains also did much and at a moment's notice were right there to write a letter or hold the hand of death. Perhaps the biggest boost to the morale were the womenfolk who came from near and far to nurse, entertain, and tidy up the place, the more enterprising going about afixing drapes to the windows and bunting and garlands to the ugly posts and rafters. Yes, just about everybody seemed to care, and this would help—help enough probably to give a man reason for living.

Superimposed on all this was the catalytic role of the hospital in the manpower shortage up at the front lines, a knotty, multi-faceted situation which neither side ever really settled. Things did tend to improve, but in war improvement is often not good enough. In a sense it seemed to be a simple case of "darned if you do and darned if you don't," for at the very time the line officers were complaining that the hospitals were holding patients too long, others maintained that sick men were being sent into battle. Confederate nurse Kate Cumming belonged to the latter group and on one occasion remarked with exquisite prophesy, "If we can not do without such men, I think the country is badly off indeed . . . "

During the first two years, a man might be discharged for the slightest reason particularly if he were chummy with the doctors or came from a state where the governor was pressuring the hospitals to get the boys back home. Again, a man might be given sick leave and never return. There were those who paid no attention to such nonsense as furloughs and discharges and just walked out, the majority never to encounter a smelly pavilion or vile latrine again. And a further twist to the hospital's plight were the vagaries of battle, for a quiet day might well be followed by weeks of slaughter, as Grant was to discover upon crossing the Rapidan. Now the hospitals would be emptied—and legitimately this time—to make room for the bleeding patients fresh from the field. The pressure in this direction is underscored by the statistic that in 1864 about one-third of the Union sick and wounded were still in field hospitals waiting for cots and beds in the general hospitals.

Both sides attempted to remedy matters in just about the same manner, and with a modicum of success. Acts were passed— too late it seems—to regulate the granting of furloughs and discharges and examining boards were established to visit the hospitals for the purpose of seeing who should stay and who should leave—that is, for home or the battlefield. In the Confederacy, the board had the power to grant furloughs up to sixty days, and to make recommendations for discharge subject to the approval of the commanding general or surgeon general. Other measures included the organization of the Invalid Corps and convalescent camps, the latter setup being a unique contribution of Civil War medicine to the wars which were to follow, in a sense hitting its acme with the World War II "rest camp." Though the convalescent camps of the first year or so not infrequently reached new heights of misery—thousands of sick men sometimes being turned out in open fields to shift for themselves—remedial measures were brought to bear and, everything considered, these camps probably did, abuses aside, help the Cause. On the one hand, they permitted the hospitals to assign their beds to the more desperate cases and, on the other, helped to stem the flow of furloughs and discharges, the idea being—and it was a good one—that if men can recover in camp, why send them home— perhaps not to return.

The Union and Confederacy both had an Invalid Corps, another interesting improvization to emerge from the war. Though its efficacy in the South can hardly be judged—probably no more than 6,000 or so men belonging—in the North there were certain favorable signs. By the close of 1863, the Yankee enrollment was somewhere around 30,000. The idea behind the corps was to utilize disabled men discharged from the hospitals in such noncombat activities as guard duty, nursing, and the like. In time, however, abuses and a "4-F complex" developed, and the Federals did the proper thing by converting the organization into a more respectable Veterans' Reserve Corps, this time concentrating on men who had served their time and looked askance at further combat, from which they were excused.

In passing, the sick and wounded officer should not be forgotten, for whereas upon the field he was often accorded preferential treatment, this was not necessarily the case once he left it. Officers were excluded from the general hospitals and thus had to look after their own medical problems—after all, they were "salaried." Besides, there is an old army axiom that men and gentlemen are not supposed to "mix," save in the heat of battle. Though some made out all right—by being cared for in their own quarters, going home, or even renting a bed at a private hospital —many were left out in the cold, sometimes literally. All of this came to a head about 1864 when the Blues and Grays decided to provide special housing. In some instances separate structures were used and in others a wing or pavilion at a general hospital was set aside. Somehow in this war things just seemed to work out, not always *on time,* but eventually.

CHAPTER VII

The Calomel Rebellion

Hɪsᴛᴏʀʏ books commonly stress primitive nineteenth century surgery yet oftentimes pay scant attention to the subject of pharmacology. For all intended purposes, the doctors and apothecaries of the 1860's knew scarcely more about drugs than did the physicians and priests of ancient times. Aside from minies and canister, the Civil War was a period of assafoetida, columbo, boneset, squill, catechu, buchu, pokeweed, Spanish fly, hog's foot oil, and anything else with a medicinal odor or interesting taste. The true situation relative to the mortar and pestle can be underscored in several ways, not the least being that sulfanilamide —the first "wonder drug"—was a good seventy-five years in the future!

The medical thinking of the past century was focused upon and mesmerized by the bowels and the kidneys and the consistency of the blood, those tangible physiologic considerations about which the doctor thought he could do something. Obviously, if a dose of this or a dose of that could force a stool or provoke a healthy stream of urine, the result had to be salutary, and so on. Since some people even today go along with this line of reasoning, the situation 100 years ago can be readily appreciated. Notwithstanding the psychological effects of eradicating body wastes, the cathartics, purgatives, and "drastics" of the Rebellion undoubtedly sent many a soldier to an early grave, as they apparently did William McKinley forty years later.

Surgeon General Hammond saw these pharmaceutical monstrosities for what they really were—another example of his genius—and struck out against calomel (mercurous chloride), the cathartic of choice right up throughout the roaring twenties. Calomel not only washes away vital fluids, as does its congeners, but also causes mercury poisoning when given too frequently— and it generally was. When Hammond ordered the drug removed from the medicine wagons and panniers, however, the doctors were shocked into disbelief and struck back in no uncertain way. The so-called "calomel rebellion" was a significant

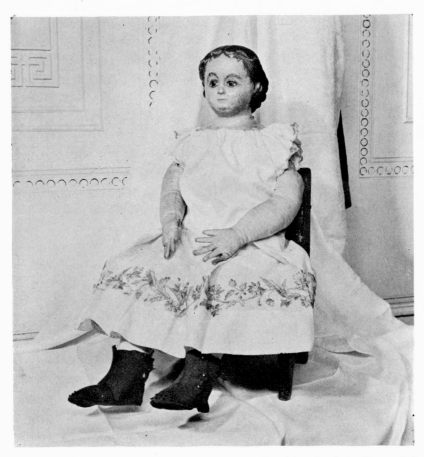

Figure 13. Nina—a large Confederate doll. In its china head, badly needed drugs were smuggled across the lines. (Confederate Museum, Richmond, Va.)

ingredient in the Surgeon General's ouster. Brilliance would be tolerated in this war, but only up to a point—and that was that. None the less, Hammond set some minds to thinking, and one wonders whether or not the omission of calomel from the drugs carried by the Army of the Potomac across the Rapidan was an unconscious or conscious act. If it were intentional, the gesture proved in vain, for the army had other kinds of laxatives and purgatives available—including "mercury pills."

Fortunately, most drugs proved harmless—as a rule—and four or five were effective enough to be what might be called "indispensable," particularly quinine, morphine, and chloroform. Quinine was the "wonder" drug of the war and the most sought after pharmaceutical in both the North and the South, whether in the pure chemical form (quinine sulfate) or in such preparations as cinchonia sulfate or cinchonia fluidextract, cinchona (bark) being the parent, or "crude," drug. Its prime use, as it is today (in those areas where the drug is still employed), was in the treatment and prevention of malaria, commonly in combination with a shot or two of whiskey. In addition, quinine was considered one of the best medicinals available for syphilis, rheumatism, neuralgia, diarrhea, and fevers, to name a few; and if there happened to be a little extra on hand, it was put to use as an antiseptic, dentifrice, gargle or hair tonic. Just exactly how good it proved to be in all these areas is a moot question, but apparently there were few complaints. At any rate, it was *bitter*—a pharmacologic response par excellence!

Opium, the pain killer of the day, was employed in pill form, the tincture (laudanum), the camphorated tincture (paregoric) or morphine, its chief active constituent. Whereas the pills and tinctures were given orally, morphine sulfate was dusted directly into wounds and sometimes injected hypodermically. The opiates were also prescribed in the management of diarrhea, a use in no way contrary to modern practice—paregoric still being a most revered medieval medicament.

In anesthesia, ether and chloroform were both used, but

chloroform was the anesthetic of choice because of its nonflammability—a consideration of no little concern during the incendi-
ary days of naked-flame illumination. It must have been a brave
surgeon, indeed, who would use ether in the rays of any light
other than those of the silvery moon. As we shall see, chloroform
apparently proved ultrasafe physiologically, an interesting piece
of information in that one would be hard put to find a bottle
of it in the modern hospital.

Other drugs of recognized efficacy in Civil War medicine
included digitalis for the heart; colchicine for gout and rheumatism; belladonna for its stimulating action upon the central
nervous system and sedative action upon the gastrointestinal tract;
and, above all, alcohol (whiskey, if you please!) —for "whatever
ails ya." With the exception of the latter, however, the aforementioned medicinals not uncommonly missed the mark for a variety
of reasons, not the least being where and when to use them. The
one apparent abuse of alcohol, and a common one, was in the
treatment of shock, a therapeutic tactic somewhat contrary to
present-day views.

Although, surprisingly, a fair number of antiseptics and
disinfectants were available, the doctors seldom employed such
antimicrobials in the right way or at the right time. After all,
few except the avant-garde had heard about microbes, and those
who had saw no reason to worry about them. In practice those
agents which nowadays we think of as antiseptics and disinfectants
were looked upon mainly as "deodorants," to use a modern term.
This explains why they were popular in the rank hospital but
not in the field and, moreover, why *antisepsis* proved to be a hit
or miss affair. Some of the more commonly used chemicals of this
character included potassium permanganate, sodium hypochlorite,
bromine, iodine, and creosote.

The shortage of some medicinals in the war conceivably
might have done more good than harm, but it was usually the
worthless concoctions which managed to stay in circulation. Alas,
the real pinch came in the short supplies of such drugs as quinine,

morphine and alcohol. The Southern states by far had the worst of it, chiefly because of Lincoln's blockade and the fact that technical know-how of drug production resided in the Union. As far as the Federals were concerned, cutting off drugs was just as effective as "giving 'em the steel," a tactic pregnant with logic but short on compassion. There were those in the North who did not feel quite right about it and some tried to get the government to change its mind, as did a Doctor Gardner at the 1863 convention of the American Medical Association. However, to his plea that "medicinal plant agents be removed from the contraband list," he was heckled and hissed away.

Possibly, the Confederate drug picture has been slightly overplayed, for every so often some prime sources relating to the subject are far from emotional, a few going so far as to deny the problem was ever what might be called *desperate*—especially in regard to chloroform. As one surgeon in the South put it, "Normally we were short (but) at times we were well-supplied." Perhaps this view falls somewhere nearer the truth.

With the exception of medicines secured through surrender and conquest, the Southerners relied principally upon purchases abroad and "internal trade" or, in a word, smuggling. This was perhaps the strangest business to which America has ever addressed itself, being in effect a floating enterprise spiked with skulduggery, greed, and sudden death.

At first, the 3,500 mile coastline of the Confederate states proved too much for the Federal blockade and for a good part of the early months of the war the sleek runners came and went pretty much as they pleased, dumping their cargoes at Mobile, Pensacola, New Orleans, Jacksonville, Galveston, Savannah, Charleston, and Wilmington, the latter two ports heading the list in traffic. During the succeeding years, however, the blockade tightened its grip and the South definitely felt the squeeze, by 1865 a ship having only about a fifty-fifty chance of making it to port.

Drugs were actually a third place item on a contraband

"want list" headed by munitions and clothing. Practically all of the business was done with England and France via pickup points at Bermuda, Nassau, and sometimes Cuba. The thing which kept it going was certainly not Confederate money, but rather cotton and tobacco. The runners themselves were manned by a hardy lot who believed in the dollar as much as the Cause, and as for the entrepreneurs, they ranged all the way from government officials to the most astute free-lancers along the coast. In the main, the profits managed to fall into private pockets, notwithstanding that most of the vessels were chartered by Richmond or the individual states.

Although the drug traffic centered on quinine, opium, morphine, chloroform, and alcoholic beverages, some cargoes were surprisingly varied, such items as acids, arsenic, sulfur, salt, copper sulfate, calomel, borax, baking soda, washing soda, bay rum, and sugar commonly being brought to port. According to government regulations, key drugs and chemicals had to be sold to the proper authorities at an established price, but in actual practice a great deal entered the black market. Speculators paid off the captains at the port city and then resold the stuff, sometimes at auction, at fantastic prices. With quinine selling at 188 dollars an ounce on the "open market"—if one could get it—it is not too difficult to imagine what the drug was doing *sub rosa,* particularly inland where most medicinals were fast disappearing from the apothecary shelves.

Much has been said and written about smuggling drugs (mainly quinine and morphine) across state lines but sometimes it is almost impossible to distinguish between fact and fiction. Even though secret compartments, phony coffins, hollow heels, hidden pockets, and petticoat hems make fascinating reading, one has good reason to queston their overall effect upon the South's pharmaceutical armamentarium. Actually, most histories favor the view that the bulk of the business with the enemy was on an "open secret" basis, for Congress early in the war authorized Lincoln to trade with the Confederacy "when it seemed advantageous." Just how much the Union realized as a result of these transactions, or the Confederacy, for that matter, is difficult to say, because most of the people engaged in the traffic were chiefly interested in their *own* profits.

In most deals, cotton was swapped for drugs, with the heaviest trading going on in and about Memphis where, according to reliable reports, millions of dollars worth of goods changed hands. As a matter of fact, business became so brisk in the city that Federal officers on more than one occasion were sufficiently embarrassed to clamp down on all activity of this nature going on at the wharves and warehouses. General Grant, in particular, was much against this sort of business and made an honest effort to drive out unauthorized promoters and speculators.

Perhaps the most interesting if not the most enterprising idea bearing on internal trade was put into operation by the Adams Express Company. For the small fee of two dollars, Adams guaranteed to deliver to any Confederate post office any quantity of quinine placed in an envelope. This proved somewhat too forward for Washington, however, and the operation was squelched soon after it had begun. Moreover, the stuff in the envelope sometimes turned out to be *morphine,* the two looking enough alike to fool a seasoned pharmacist. Of course, this type of thing could and did happen at all levels of drug smuggling.

At the outset, the South had no pharmaceutical plants to speak of, and, as a result, Surgeon General Moore ordered the establishment of government facilities at Mobile, Charleston, Columbia, Augusta, and a few other cities. (Certain states, too, put up plants for the purpose.) Here alcohol, acids, silver nitrate, potassium iodide, ether, and a few other chemicals were manufactured, and smuggled-in medicines—chiefly, opium, morphine, and quinine—were tested for strength and purity. Since the output was obviously dependent upon suitable raw chemicals (scarce themselves), the principal contribution of these laboratories to the Cause appears to have been analysis control. The druggist came into his own at this time, not only in manipulating intricate polypharmacal mixtures, but also in searching for drug substitutes.

Indigenous substitutes, interestingly enough, were a hallmark of Confederate medicine. Wrote the surgeon general, "Our forests and savannahs furnish our materia medica with a moderate number of narcotics and sedatives and an abundant number of tonics, astringents, aromatics, and demulcents . . . " The apothecary scrutinized his dusty jars; the Ladies' Aid Societies tried their hand at medicinal gardening; and the common folk, following Surgeon Moore's dictum, combed the meadows and forests. In the course of the four years, the number of different things tried assuredly outnumbered those which were not, but whether anybody ever discovered anything of value is lost to history: Cucumbers for burns, pokeweed for camp itch, geranium for diarrhea, persimmons for dysentery, charcoal for diphtheria . . . The favorite tonic, appropriately dubbed "old indigenous," contained dogwood bark, poplar bark, willow bark, and whiskey. Above all, it was terribly bitter—just like *quinine!*

Except for an occasional scarcity of quinine, the Federals for the most part were able to get the drugs they needed via purchases abroad and manufacturing facilities here at home. By 1862, the Medical Department Standard Supply Table could boast of 131 preparations—a new world record! We can get some idea of the business volume by taking a look at the issued amounts of certain key medicaments: for example, Epsom salt (540,000 lbs.) , copaiba (80,000 lbs.), and whiskey (160,000 qts.).

The private firms of note included Edward R. Squibb, John Wyeth and Brother, Philip Schieffelin and Company, McKesson and Robbins, and Charles Pfizer and Company—outfits whose medicines still grace the corner apothecary. Also, there were a good number of quack concerns about, pushing their pills and elixirs with as much success at the sutler's as at the general store back on Main Street. Holloway's Pills, for instance, cured "anything and everything," and Dr. Forsha's tonic worked wonders for gunshot wounds, or so President Lincoln tried to convince Surgeon General Hammond.

Somewhat to the consternation of private interests, the government, at the insistence of Surgeon General Hammond, decided to go into the drug business, and in 1863 established laboratories at Philadelphia, Pennsylvania and Astoria, New York. Wrote the director of the Philadelphia Laboratory to Hammond, " . . . The manufacturing chemists here in Philadelphia are in a great stew about our laboratories, especially as they know that I am trying to estimate the cost of manufacturing quinine. Their squirming shows that their profits have been enormous." Indeed, this might well have been the whole idea behind the government plants, that is, to keep prices in check by "threatening" at any moment to expand. Quinine, the number one "wonder drug," for instance, dropped seventy cents an ounce even before the laboratories were placed into operation.

The Philadelphia establishment was an elaborate affair and a showplace for the gadgetry of the coming chemical age—glistening copper kettles, gigantic stills, steam-operated grinders, and, of all things, stirring machines. Though Surgeon Smith, the director, was neither a chemist nor pharmacist himself, he managed to secure the best brains in the business. John M. Maisch and C. Lewis Diehl, in particular, stand out, for almost single-handedly they developed ingenious processes and techniques for the manufacture and control of quality medicinals. After the war, Maisch became the first permanent secretary of the American Pharmaceutical Association and Diehl, a graduate of the Philadelphia College of Pharmacy (now the Philadelphia College of Pharmacy and Science, the country's oldest [1821] school of pharmacy) helped to spark the development of the National Formulary, to this day a bible of pharmaceutical practice.

In February of 1865, the laboratory at Astoria went up in flames, and not long thereafter, the Philadelphia plant was "decommissioned." Interestingly enough, although a few in the military and Washington expressed a certain hope that the government would stay in the drug business, the specter of socialized medicine was in the wind even then. The men who had directed and managed the plants were commended for their "faithful and meritorious service"—everybody except for Maisch and Diehl. The laboratories themselves experienced a similar demise for, despite the pleas of William Proctor, America's father of pharmacy, they were accorded but two small paragraphs in the Official Records. Was this another slap at Hammond?

A man worthy of special mention was Edward Squibb, founder of E. R. Squibb and Sons—today one of the world's great drug houses. Squibb, a physician, not only had extraordinary inventive genius, but also a keen nose for business, as the people in Washington were soon to discover. A few years prior to the war, Squibb perfected "mass production" methods for the manufacture of ether and chloroform at Brooklyn's U. S. Naval Hospital Laboratory and, together with Naval Surgeon Benjamin F. Bache, pioneered in setting up drug standards, a *sine qua non* in the manufacture of pharmaceuticals. Doctor Squibb's concern received the bulk of the army contracts, somewhat to the dismay of other private firms, principally because, comparatively speaking, it had the power to deliver top-notch quality on short notice. Too, the Federal laboratories were employing certain Squibb methods of production, and the politicians in Washington might very well have wished to "show their appreciation."

In addition to quinine and anesthetics, Squibb sold to the Medical Department (for 110 dollars) a cowhide pannier stocked with fifty-two medicines and a conglomeration of odds and ends— condensed milk, sponges, oiled silk, spatulas, tourniquets, candles, matches, to name a few. In most commands, it was customary to issue one pannier to each regiment, whether Squibb's, Dunton's, or another's.

The subject of supply, however, is certainly not confined to the amassing of goods, for unless there are efficient means of distribution, the consequences—in war, at least—prove negative in a most unqualified way. A bottle of chloroform in Charleston, for instance, does pathetically little for a man getting his leg sawed off at Chickamauga.

Early in the war, the Blues and the Grays put into operation a supply system of almost identical organization, a system which, everything considered, was just about as good as the facilities the respective camps would permit. In the North, major medical depots were established at Philadelphia and New York, which in turn supplied (via railroad) Washington, Baltimore, St. Louis, Chicago, New Orleans, Nashville, Memphis, and some twenty other locations. A so-called "medical purveyor" was the man in charge, and he had the trying chore of stocking the depot, often on a most capricious budgetary schedule, with medicines, surgical instruments, and general hospital supplies. From the depots, the goods, via rail or mule train, made their way to the battle area where the field purveyors, who were usually hospital stewards, replenished the medicine wagons (the *Perot* and *Autenrieth* wagons being the most famous). One wagon was assigned to a brigade, and it was the brigade surgeon's duty to see that each regiment had its knapsacks and panniers well-stocked. The whole system depended heavily on the cooperation of the Quartermaster Department and, generally speaking, this was the case. The chief supply problem, it developed, was in not having movable depots and field hospitals. However, this now seems to have been a sign of the times more than anything else, and quite inevitable.

Confederate Surgeon Moore also appointed purveyors and set up depots at strategic locations. The big problem, though, was getting the stuff to the field, there being a dearth of wagons and animals to pull them. Napoleon's remark that, "the enemy has everything and we need everything," always hit home—each time with greater force, it seemed.

CHAPTER VIII

Remarkable and Frightful

Over the four bitter years, the North and South tangled with each other 2,196 times amidst such madness that on occasion the musketry alone felled a forest. Somewhere around 67,000 Federals were killed outright, 43,000 died of wounds, and some 130,000 were scarred or disfigured for life. Among the Confederates, the best figures indicate that somewhere in the vicinity of 94,000 died of wounds. For both sides the minie ball was responsible 94 per cent of the time and shell and canister about 6 per cent of the time. The snarling sabre and bayonet proved quite harmless, producing a sum total of only 922 Federal wounds throughout the entire war, and of these only fifty-six were fatal.

According to one school of thought, wounded men are a greater liability to the opposing army than dead ones, a thesis underscored by the order, "Fire at their feet!" If this were modified to include the arms, perhaps we could attempt in part to account for the relative frequency of wounds cited in the Official Records, which show 35.1 per cent involved the arms and 35.7 per cent the legs. In other words, roughly three out of four wounded Federals were hit in the extremities, and there is every reason to believe the same proportion obtained among the Confederates. Wounds of the trunk and those of the head (face and neck) accounted for 18.4 per cent and 10.7 per cent respectively. Another explanation, cited by some, for these disparities is that, when firing from "protected" positions—felled trees, breastworks, and the like—the extremities are more exposed than the head or trunk.

Penetrating gunshot wounds of the abdomen and head were about 90 per cent fatal. In the event the small intestine was involved, death was inevitable as a consequence of a fulminating peritonitis, *except* in the case of the Confederate lad at Gettysburg who was shot in the abdomen and hours later passed the ball in the stool—and lived to tell about it. Penetrating wounds of the chest had a better prognosis than one might expect, with a mortality in the vicinity of 60 per cent. Flesh wounds, everything considered, fared surprisingly well. For all types of wounds, superficial as well as penetrating, the Official Records show 49 per cent mortality for the abdomen and 28 per cent each for the head and the chest. Shot wounds of the spine proved to be 56 per cent fatal. What statistics are available for the Confederacy show similar trends of mortality.

The minie, or, as the Official Records prefer to call it, "conoidal ball," often produced a more savage wound than the lead missile of the twentieth century for the somewhat paradoxical reason that it traveled at a slower speed. Whereas the .30 caliber bullet of World War I and World War II fame drilled a nice neat hole and often passed right through the body, the minie plodded into the interior tagged along with pieces of clothing and skin. It was well put in the colorful view of one surgeon: " . . . the shattering, splintering, and splitting of a long bone by the impact of the minie were, in many instances, both remarkable and frightful . . . "

Extensive bleeding and shock were common and infection was assured, the latter of relatively minor consequence today but ominous at that time. Ironically, the velocity of the modern bullet is such that it may well sterilize itself via friction-generated heat as it passes through the air. In short, if the minie failed to effect outright death it could always leave the job to the staphylococcus.

After all has been said, it might appear that no one dreamed of microbes during those terrifying years, but such was by no means the case. The concept of infection is ancient and many

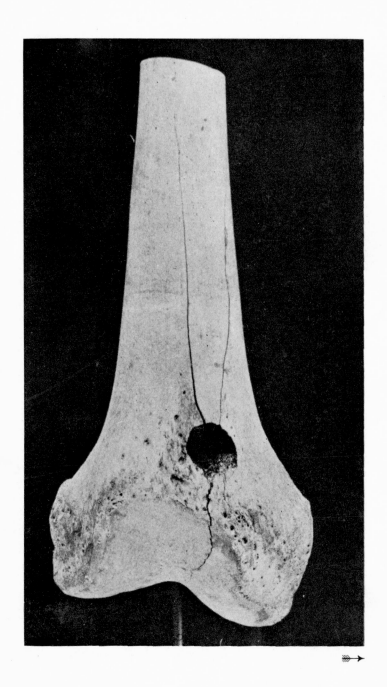

observant doctors prior to and during the Civil War were becoming highly suspicious of those invisible enemies. Years before the war, Oliver Wendell Holmes underscored in print the contagiousness of puerperal, or childbed, fever, and in 1861 the brilliant Ignaz Semmelweis of Vienna demonstrated that this scourge of childbirth was an *infectious* disease incited by those attending the mother. Although Semmelweis in no uncertain manner proved the value of clean hands, few doctors were much impressed. This was strange, indeed, for some surgeons had publicized the close relationship between puerperal fever and the so-called "surgical fevers." Try as he would, Doctor William Detmold, for instance, could not convince any sizable audience. And it becomes even more provocative that the complications of surgery were generally considered to be infections—infections caused by mysterious airborne "noxious effluvia" rather than sticky bloody hands or pus-smeared knives!

In all fairness, though, the idea of noxious effluvia did imply an external cause—certainly a big step in the right direction—and did, moreover, lead to a mania for fresh air and the eradication of malodorous emanations. In turn this led to the widespread use of deodorants, many unwittingly being excellent antiseptics. Alcohol, carbolic acid, iodine, bromine, mercuric chloride, acids, and sodium hypochlorite were all used. Interestingly enough, sodium hypochlorite, in the form of Dakin's solution, was hailed

---

Figure 14. *Perforation of the Right Femur, just above the Condyles, by a Musket Ball.* Private Samuel S. Kopp, E, 10th Pennsylvania Reserves, was shot through the lower third of the right thigh, by a musket ball, at the second battle of Bull Run, August 28, 1862. The ball entered just above the patella, and made its exit in the popliteal space. The patient was taken, after a few days, to Alexandria, and admitted to General Hospital. On September 20, 1862, his thigh was amputated at the middle by Surgeon Charles Page, U. S. A. He survived the operation two days. The specimen, No. 76, Surgical Section, presents a very good example of a gunshot perforation through the cancellated portion of a long bone. Two fissures, which extend through the diaphysis, are seen running to the middle third of the shaft. A narrower fissures separates the condyles. (The Armed Forces Institute of Pathology [2-761].)

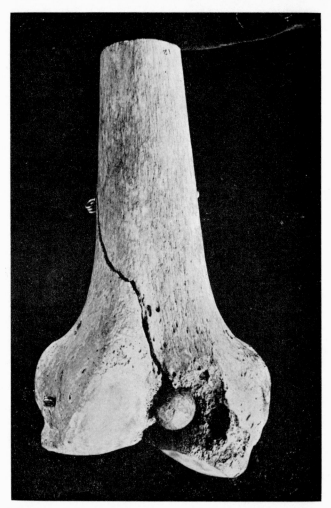

Figure 15. *Lower Third of Right Femur, the Outer Condyle split off by a
Roman Musket Ball. Amputation. Death.* Private Richard Williams, 28th
Pennsylvania, was wounded September 16, 1862, at the battle of South
Mountain, by a round musket ball, which entered near the outer hamstring
and lodged between the condyles of the right femur. He was conveyed to
Washington, and admitted into Mount Pleasant Hospital, September 22,
1862. On September 30th, his right thigh was amputated, by flap incisions.
At this date the limb was excessively swollen: the discharge of pus was
profuse, abscesses had burrowed in the soft parts, and irritative fever
existed to an alarming degree. The case terminated fatally on October 2, 1862.
The ball, which remained imbedded in the cancellated structure of the
femur, between the condyles, had caused a very oblique fracture into the
knee-joint, separating the external condyle from the shaft, and breaking
off a fragment from the anterior surface of the inner condyle. (The Armed
Forces Institute of Pathology [12-59].)

as the miracle drug of World War I and is still considered by some a good antiseptic for raw wounds. Its efficacy depends upon the release of chlorine, just about the most potent anti-infective known. Unfortunately, the Civil War surgeon used it as Labarraque's solution, a preparation ten times stronger than Dakin's solution and extremely irritating. Essentially, Labarraque's solution was just about the same stuff as the liquid bleach sold at the supermarket.

In most instances, these agents were applied liberally to just about everything in the operating area except for the surgeon's hands and instruments. Unclean hands, knives, and saws on occasion got a dose or two, and it was probably under just these circumstances that surgeon "so and so" in department "so and so" obtained such good results. Certainly Ignaz Semmelweis, the man who was trying to be heard, did and in the obstetrical ward of Vienna's Allgemeines Krankenhause, he decreased the incidence of puerperal fever from 11 per cent to 1 per cent by ordering medical students (who were prone to come directly from autopsies) to wash ther dirty hands in chlorinated water. But the Rebellion was not the Allgemeines Krankenhause and, besides, filthy instruments would do—provided they were good and sharp. If the nurses and matrons wanted to wash out the urinals and slop buckets with sodium hypochlorite, it was perfectly all right with the surgeons, but as for themselves they had no time for such effluvial matters—there was too much cutting to be done. About this there could be no argument.

In substance, then, Civil War sepsis did not stem from a lack of antiseptics but rather from a lack of *antisepsis*. In other words, had any one of the antimicrobials mentioned above been used in the right way and at the right time, the forces of nature would have had a fighting chance. Even the best antiseptic must be applied *before*—not after.

The doctors and nurses were not long in gaining a respect for the surgical fevers, and in time achieved a slight measure of success in their control. Noxious effluvia were fought against,

isolation was practiced, and in the better thinking establishments soupy exudates—with the exception of "laudable pus," of course— and mean-looking wounds, incisions, and stumps were considered most unfavorable. Some surgeons even progressed to the point where they refused to operate during a bout of hospital gangrene. But contaminated fingers continued to probe the open wounds and incisions, and the soiled instruments remained soiled.

Even among the most knowledgeable surgeons, the general feeling was that wounds exuding odorless creamy pus (usually emblematic of *Staphylococcus aureus*) were doing well. It was simply nature's way of getting rid of bad tissue and recalcitrant humors. From an 1865 case study found in the Official Records: " . . . the wound discharging healthy pus and granulating finely . . . " In a word it was an era of laudable pus. But it was to the credit of most doctors, stewards, and nurses that wayward exudations, that is, the off-color and smelly ones, were not held in such high esteem. Indeed, these were considered not only unhealthy but also a prime source of those deadly miasmas and noxious effluvia.

The usual infectious consequences of wounds and surgical manipulations were osteomyelitis, erysipelas, gangrene, and pyemia. From what the bacteriologist can deduce from the case histories and practices of the time, these vicious infections are believed to have been spawned in the main by *Staphylococcus*

Figure 16. *Amputated Portion of Left Femur, with a Leaden Ball in the Medullary Canal.* At the battle of Chancellorsville, on May 3, 1863, Brigadier General Edmund K———, U. S. V., First Lieutenant, 1st U. S. Artillery, was wounded by two leaden balls from a spherical case shot, which entered the lower part of the left thigh. One of the missiles fractured the femur and was impacted in its medullary canal, the other lodged in the vastus externus. The wounded man was conveyed to Washington on May 5th, and, on May 10th, Surgeon Basil Norris, U. S. A., amputated the thigh by the circular method. Pyaemia supervened, and death on May 28, 1863. The specimen, No. 1076 of the Surgical Section, was contributed by the operator, and is one of the few illustrations in the Museum, of the lodging of balls in the medullary cavity of long bones. (The Armed Forces Institute of Pathology [163-1076].)

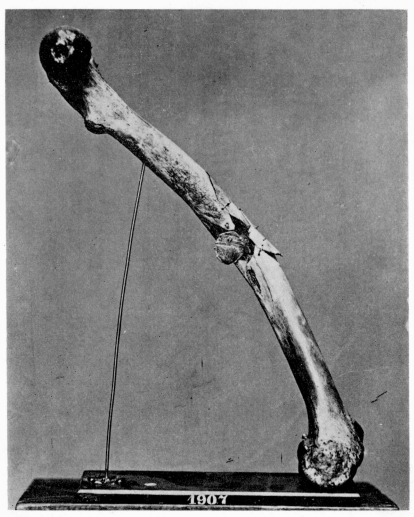

Figure 17. *Comminuted Gunshot Fracture of the Left Femur by a Conoidal Ball, which had previously passed through the Right Thigh. Death, sixteen days after the injury.* Private John Draker, Company I, 57th Regiment Pennsylvania Volunteers, 25 years old, was wounded while on picket duty on the Rapidan, November 27th, 1863. A conoidal musket ball passed through the muscles of the right thigh, and, entering the middle of the left thigh at its inner side, flattened itself against the femur, and shattered the bone. The patient was transferred to Alexandria by rail, and admitted December 4th, 1863, to the Second Division U. S. A. General Hospital. He died December 13th, 1863. The specimen is a good example of a comminuted fracture of the shaft of a long bone by a projectile moving with diminished velocity. No attempt at repair. (The Armed Forces Institute of Pathology [4-1907].)

aureus and *Streptococcus pyogenes,* ubiquitous bacterial cells which generate pus, destroy tissue, and release deadly toxins. Locally, these germs are bad enough, but once in the blood they multiply rapidly and eventually pepper the body inside and out with myriad abscesses. This is pyemia, and in a hail of chills, sweat, fever, and advancing jaundice the patient gallops to his death. Of 2,818 reported cases of this pus-wrought malady, in the Union army only seventy-one men recovered. Among the Confederates it is said to have been responsible for about 35 per cent of all deaths following amputation. The cases of erysipelas, now generally accepted as being caused by *Streptococcus pyogenes,* were probably diagnosed correctly in most instances because of the characteristic reddening and swelling of the affected areas. Though assuredly not as lethal as pyemia, erysipelas did, in the wake of the saw and knife, kill a large number of men. In a typical example, out of 236 diagnosed cases of the disease, twenty-two died. In addition to drainage and cold water treatment of the eruptive lesions, the patients were given "stimulating" food and lots of whiskey.

Regarding gangrene, one has to actually see it and smell it to believe it! In brief, it is simply a rotting away of the flesh caused by the obstruction of the blood flow to some part of the body, generally the foot, or by bacterial invasion. The former variety is the less nasty, particularly if it is not pounced upon by secondary microbial invaders. The bacterial variety of the battlefield, or gas gangrene, is caused by certain species *(Clostridia)* which gain entrance to the tissues via deep dirty wounds. The form of the infection, however, which raged through Civil War hospitals in epidemic proportions—the form which struck clean wounds and incisions—may well have been caused by *Streptococcus pyogenes.* As a matter of fact, as the years passed by, many surgeons were beginning to suspect a common denominator among erysipelas, pyemia, and hospital gangrene; and well they should, for *Streptococcus pyogenes* can, in one way or another, cause all three.

Hospital gangrene, as it was called (now extinct in hospitals worthy of the name), blazed throughout the wards with the fury of fire and destroyed vulnerable tissue en masse. The afflicted area of the body turned greenish, bluish, grayish, blackish, and shades thereof, and exuded a devilish mush that stank to the highest of heavens. The Official Records cite 2,642 cases of this creeping black death, of which 1,142 proved fatal (46 per cent).

Every surgeon seemed to have had a pet approach to hospital gangrene, some using the knife, some corrosive chemicals—nitric acid was a favorite!—and some miscellaneous items such as chlorine, turpentine, yeast, charcoal, and the like. Of special interest was the discovery by Yankee surgeon Middleton Goldsmith of the efficacy of bromine, an element very closely related to chlorine and iodine. In his "Report on Hospital Gangrene, Erysipelas, and Pyemia as Observed in the Department of Ohio and the Cumberland," a paper written more than three years before that of Lord Lister's revelations, Goldsmith described how the application of bromine checked the ravages of gangrene in the hospitals under his charge. Bromine was less drastic than nitric acid and, in the words of the surgeon, " . . . respirable without injury or inconvenience." Moreover, according to one study, of 334 cases treated with bromine the fatality rate was only three per cent, as against 62 per cent for nitric acid. Goldsmith's findings were corroborated by others and by the end of the war the treatment was generally adopted among the Federal hospitals.

But the signal feature of Goldsmith's bromine related to its prophylactic possibilities, a disclosure many hospitals were putting into use. It was sprayed into the air—to counteract the effluvia—and some doctors and nurses discovered that painting abrasions of the hands with bromine solutions drastically cut down the likelihood of contracting gangrene from their patients. Others were beginning to use sodium hypochlorite for the same purpose. Such practices plus the growing trend toward isolation and the use of uncontaminated sponges and dressings proved so effective that by 1865 no epidemics of hospital gangrene were reported among the Federals.

Turning to the surgeons of the South, in addition to the scalpel and nitric acid, maggots were used in gangrene, a discovery made originally by Napoleon's medics. Maggots—fly larvae developed from eggs deposited in decaying matter, decaying flesh being a choice medium—release a chemical called *allantoin* which brings about the digestion of necrotic material, thereby promoting the growth of new tissue. The Union doctors, understandably repulsed by these unsightly white, wiggly, wormy-looking creatures, got rid of them with chloroform, as did the Confederates until an alert surgeon ran out of the stuff, and discovered quite accidentally that maggots are efficient scavengers. This unique cleansing technique, today known as "chemical debridement" and accomplished by such potent necrotic digestants as Varidase, Elase, Tryptar, was popular right up through World War I, where maggots were employed to treat osteomyelitis and and other suppurative infections.

"His teeth came together with a crash and the lad passed away in that struggle . . . " The struggle was tetanus (or "lockjaw"), a vicious and rapidly fatal disease caused by the bacterium, *Clostridium tetani*. As a consequence of a deep puncture wound, spores of the microbe may be introduced into the air-free tissues where they undergo rapid development and multiplication. Superficial wounds are less likely to incite the infection because of the presence of air and oxygen, the latter serving to inhibit the organism. Once a focus of infection has been established, this insidious germ releases a fantastically lethal toxin which acts upon the nervous system causing convulsions and locking of the jaw.

But few indeed died in that struggle, a most unusual finding in light of the fact that stepping on a tack can prove fatal even today. For the entire war, the Official Records cite no more than 505 cases of tetanus, and quite likely there were about this number among the Confederates. Of course, there undoubtedly were undiagnosed cases, but not enough to substantially alter the basic picture when the astronomical number of serious wounds is taken into consideration. One explanation emphasizes that, in the main, the battles were fought on unplowed and unmanured fields, manure being the chief source of clostridial spores. Further, just about all cases of tetanus stemmed from battlefields where the wounded were cared for in stables and barns with ankle-deep manure. Here the mortality ran close to ninety per cent, just about what it is today in unprotected or untreated victims. Because of the universal use of tetanus toxoid during World War II, it is said, not a single American soldier died of the disease.

The above reasoning probably applies also to the dearth of Civil War gas gangrene, the most troublesome wound complication encountered in World War I. Like *Clostridium tetani* the causative agent *(Clostridium perfringens)* is present in manured soil and abhors oxygen.

Another topic central to the study of Civil War wounds is bandaging. While in the field the procedure generally had little sophistication—at the battle of Antietam corn leaves were used—in the hospital it developed into somewhat of an art, especially among the doctors who strove to demonstrate their medical prowess. The favorite dressing was lint, a soft absorbent material made by scraping (with a knife) or picking apart old woven linen. It was usually applied wet, covered with cheesecloth or muslin, and held in place with adhesive plaster. Among the southern states the supply frequently ran short with the result that raw cotton was used as a substitute. Processed by *oven-baking* the finished product turned out, unwittingly, to be essentially sterile, an advantage noted on occasion but not fully appreciated or understood. Similarly, the shortage in the South of surgical silk led to the use of horsehair—which had to be *boiled* to render it soft and pliable—and the shortage of sponges led to the use of rags. This was interesting, too, for unlike a filthy sponge, a filthy rag had a better chance of coming out of the wash less contaminated.

Conditions in the field were never really good. Old bandages heavily laden with every microbe under the sun were often used again and again and, worst of all, it apparently just never occurred to anyone to supply the individual soldier with emergency dressings. Until treatment arrived, a piece of torn shirt or sticky handkerchief had to do.

In addition to bandaging, the nonsurgical treatment of wounds relied principally upon the use of cold water, a practice highly regarded by both medical services. The reports that cold water applied by either irrigation or constant drip (over the bandage) "proved invaluable" in the management of gunshot wounds and deep lacerations are somewhat in accord with modern thinking. A typical case was that of a lad who had a large chunk of his chest wall blown out and for hours lay in shock on the battlefield. Solely through the use of water compresses he pulled through. The late Doctor Mont Rogers Reid, a world authority on the handling of wounds, believed that sometimes "too much emphasis is placed on antiseptics—agents which often hinder healing."

Not all surgeons, however, were sold on the idea of cold water, some strongly advocating dry lint and others open air. Although not as soothing as cold water, these modes of therapy certainly had their advantages on occasion. Using dry dressings, one surgeon claimed he had but one case of gangrene among 650 patients, and at Gettysburg the Confederate wounded are said to have fared well with no other treatment than the air which blankets the earth. Today the open-air treatment *of burns* is looked upon as a signal therapeutic advancement.

The control of bleeding centered upon ligation, heavy bandaging, and liberal application of coagulants, or styptics, the latter including such chemical agents as silver nitrate, tannic acid, alum, ferric sulfate, and ferric chloride. Tincture of ferric chloride enjoyed wide use well into the present century. As for the replacement of lost blood, about the best that could be done for the patient was the feeding of liberal portions of "stimulating" food, if available. For the control of pain, said to have been most pronounced a day or two after the wound had been received, opium and morphine were used, morphine sulfate generally being rubbed right into the raw tissue or occasionally injected. At the Turner's Lane Hospital in Philadelphia, Surgeons S. Weir Mitchell, George Moorhouse, and William W. Keen found that leeches placed directly on nerve trunks did much to lessen pain. These men also advocated the use of morphine to control neuralgia, and a combination of morphine and atropine to quieten the exicted patient.

An interesting side light was the "revolutionary" and hotly debated practice introduced by Federal Surgeon Benjamin Howard of hermetically sealing gunshot wounds of the chest. The technique was simply to plug the hole with lint and then make it airtight with collodion. Since an opening in the chest cavity causes collapse of the lung, the procedure no doubt did, as Surgeon Howard argued, "relieve extreme dyspnea" (labored breathing). However, at one and the same time it also hindered drainage and fostered microbial multiplication. Paradoxically, the Confederates thought highly of the hermetic approach and in the words of Surgeon J. J. Chisolm, "It was the almost universal adoption of this surgical procedure in all wounded cases that yielded us our splendid results." In contrast, Surgeon General Barnes observed in the Official Records, "Hermetic sealing was fairly tested during the war and its indiscriminate application found to be pernicious . . . "

Severe shot wounds of the extremities usually resulted in bone fracture, an event which not uncommonly led to amputation. Undoubtedly, had better splints been more generally available, the results would have been much improved, a finding underscored in no uncertain way on the positive side during World Wars I and II. A good splint is essential both as a first aid measure to immobilize the parts temporarily and as a means of maintaining fixation of the parts until union of the injured bone occurs.

Nevertheless, things could have been worse in this direction,

and toward the end of the war orthopedic progress was being made. The shortage of "G.I. splints," particularly in the Confederacy, proved to be another instance where necessity served as the mother of invention. Boards, wire, straw, sheets of metal, and even the bark of trees were used, sometimes with striking success. The most outstanding advance, though, related to the general acceptance of *plaster of Paris*—a material which to this day has not been improved upon—and the introduction in 1863 of the famous Hodgen splint, a device still used in the treatment of fractures of the lower femur. A modification of Nathan Smith's anterior suspension splint, the Hodgen is an arrangement consisting of a simple steel bar frame with pulleys and a cord that secures traction and permits suspension, flexion, and rotation. Above all, Hodgen's splint gave maximum comfort to the patient and allowed for proper nursing care of the wound without disturbing the fracture. Union Surgeon John Hodgen, by instinct and inclination a good mechanic as well as a good doctor, also invented a forceps to remove foreign bodies from the trachea, a suspension splint for arm fractures, a hairpin dilator for windpipe wounds, a double action syringe, and a stomach pump.

CHAPTER IX

Arms and Legs Galore

T HE well-known Federal surgeon, John H. Brinton, relates how a distraught hayfoot-strawfoot volunteer surgeon under his command pleaded with him to assist in an amputation. It seems the volunteer had never even held a knife, much less a saw. Several months later Brinton discovered in no uncertain terms that he had been a good teacher: "I found bloodstained footmarks on the crooked stairs of a two-story little country house and in the second story room stood *my friend;* arms and legs seemed almost to litter the floor; beneath the operating table was a pool of blood, the operator was smeared with it and the surroundings were ghastly beyond all limits of surgical propriety. 'Ah Doctor,' said the new-fledged surgeon, 'I am getting on, just look at these,' pointing to his trophies on the floor with a right regal gesture . . . "

Before long the doctors on both sides were "getting on," and by Gettysburg most had become seasoned choppers. In the wake of that slaughter of slaughters, General Schurz recalled " . . . the surgeon snatched the knife from between his teeth, wiped it across his bloodstained apron, and the cutting began . . . "

In the surgery of Civil War vintage, the only important ally of the operator and his patient was nature herself, for the good work of the medicine men of ancient Greece and Rome had not only been ignored, but also appreciably undone. Although the Arabs and Jews had kept alive much that was valuable from early surgery, a schism between the physician and surgeon forced surgical practice into the hands of the unskilled, untutored, and

90

itinerant. In essence, the physician became a man of science and the surgeon evolved into a charlatan or part-time barber. And here the scalpel and saw remained until the latter part of the nineteenth century.

At the time of the Rebellion there were, it is true, sparks of good thinking and even an occasional noteworthy accomplishment, but this essentially was cloistered knowledge. Thus, to a degree, it was a case of there not being enough teachers and textbooks around to put surgery—and medicine, for that matter—on an even keel. And, of course, the situation proved worse in America than in Europe, where schools of medicine had already started to attract outstanding surgeons. The doctors in Europe, moreover, were beginning to vent their ideas in printed form, and had it not been for this overseas literature, the medical service in both camps would have been worse off than it actually was. Certainly,

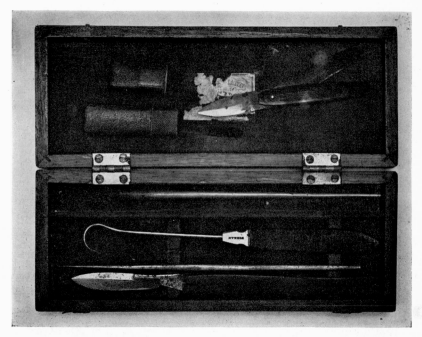

Figure 18. Confederate pocket surgical kit. (Confederate Museum, Richmond, Va.)

one is struck by the know-how and many accomplishments among the surgeons who read. In point of fact, at the start of the conflict, the best available information came from such works as MacLeod's *Notes on the Surgery of the War in the Crimea* and Matthew's *Medical and Surgical History of the British Army.* Indeed, these particular sources stimulated the development of a number of domestic publications and, *in time,* manuals of medicine and surgery were available in most areas. Everything considered, some of these, for instance, Chisolms' *A Manual of Military Surgery for the Use of Surgeons in the Confederate Army* and Warren's *An Epitome of Practical Surgery for Field and Hospital,* could be held as classics.

Nothing relating to Civil War surgery can approach the stature of the *surgical fevers,* not even the saw-happy apprentice or the tubs of slimy blood. The body puts up a good fight against just about everything save such microscopic agents of death as *Streptococcus pyogenes* and *Staphylococcus aureus.* "Staph" even today plague the best of operating rooms and continue to thwart the efforts of the chemists. When we consider that a single healthy carrier of *Stapylococcus aureus*—several feet removed from the operating table and in an otherwise aseptic environment—can infect the surgical field, the Civil War situation comes into better focus. In short, the surgeons in blue and gray were meat cutters— or butchers, if that term can be used without malice—who acted like meat cutters. They washed their hands only when smelly or sticky and wiped off their knives and saws only when the day was done. William Keen, an outstanding Federal surgeon, once remarked, "Surgeons always imperiled life and often actually caused death . . . " Of course, the aides did their bit too. Messy incisions were washed with messy water and oozing tissues sponged with oozing sponges. As a Confederate surgeon said after the war, "One blessing we enjoyed, due to the blockade, was the absence of sponges . . . "

The view is sometimes expressed that if the Civil War had been fought just a few years later, the post-operative horrors of

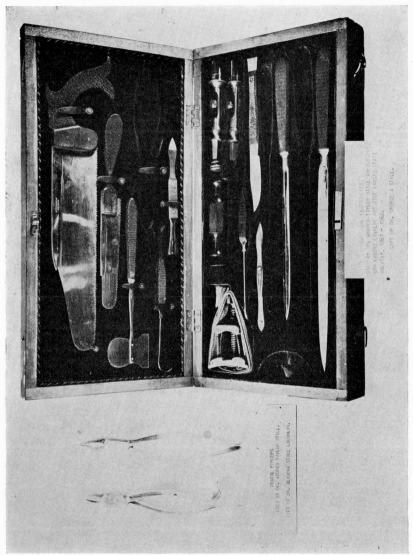

Figure 19. Surgical instruments case used by Dr. Andrew Taylor Still during the Civil War. (M-1470 in Smithsonian Collection, Division of Medical Sciences.)

infection would have been largely averted. But this seems to be calling it much too close, since the concept of antiseptic surgery (circa 1867) did not flash around the world by any means. And besides, Lister's carbolic acid is a fairly primitive substance, relatively weak antiseptically and relatively dangerous toxicologically. Further, *antiseptic* methods were only the beginning, for surgery did not enter its modern, or *aseptic,* phase until the introduction of steam sterilization by Ernst von Bergmann in 1882. Rubber gloves did not come along until the turn of the century, when the American surgeon William Halsted had a pair specially made to protect the chapped hands of his nurse fiancée.

Although the topic of anesthesia attracts the layman's attention, from a standpoint of life and death it is possibly a poor second to asepsis. Man can endure a lot of pain if he has to, and history tells us that all kinds of major surgery were performed centuries before William Morton's ether demonstration at Boston's Massachusetts General Hospital in 1846. In 1809, for example, the American surgeon Ephriam McDowell removed an ovarian tumor without the benefit of any anesthetic! None the less, few patients care to witness themselves being sawed up, and with relatively few exceptions no one had to in the Civil War. Anesthesia was "well understood" and, legend to the contrary, the supply of ether and chloroform was adequate in the North and generally so in the South. Obviously, shortages occurred when the wagon trains got bogged down in the mud or supplies were captured by the enemy, as was the case at the battle of Winchester where Stonewall Jackson's men ran off with 15,000 cases of chloroform. (The Confederates, as a matter of fact, were dependent upon this type of source.)

According to the Surgeon General of the United States, there were no less than 80,000 instances in the Union medical service where anesthesia was used, and chloroform, due to its nonflammability and speed of action, was the anesthetic of choice in both armies. In the study which appears in the Official Records, of 8,900 operations, Federal surgeons used chloroform in 6,784, a mixture of ether and chloroform in 1,305, and ether alone in 811 cases. And the results, taking them at their face value, were somewhat fantastic, there being only thirty-seven deaths among the cases cited. And in the South, only two chloroform deaths were reported! After the war, a Confederate doctor exclaimed, "The safety of the substance was remarkable when you consider how loosely it was used!" This is a central point for, granting a number of post-operative circulatory and hepatic complications (which certainly must have occurred because chloroform is hard on both the heart and liver), it would seem, in light of present-day views relating to this sweet-smelling liquid, that more "should have passed away on the table." In a way, it sounds like the child who plays with matches and fails to get burned.

The technique for administering chloroform and ether was the acme of simplicity, referred to by today's anesthetist as the "open method." The liquid was sprinkled onto a sponge, handkerchief or cotton cloth which was held in place over the patient's nose and mouth, a funnel sometimes being used as an inhaler to prevent excessive evaporation. Substituting gauze for the handkerchief and a cone or wire mask for the funnel, the technique becomes quite modern. Though a far cry from the elaborate plumbing involved in the administration of anesthetic gases, the open method in the proper setting is still an efficient and safe method of anesthesia.

The anesthetic was forced until the patient was limp, a crude but none the less "fairly accurate" way to signal surgical anesthesia. Since it was common practice to give a good dosing with whiskey prior to the anesthetic—especially to those in shock —the anesthetic requirement was appreciably reduced. Although *preanesthetic medication* (to use the modern expression) is certainly sound medicine, in that it dulls the senses and allays apprehension, it is considered bad business in shock since alcohol tends to further reduce the blood pressure. Again, however, this was the Civil War, not Bellevue Hospital, and nature's rules on not a few occasions appear to have been different. Either that, or we have a lot to learn, and in the instance of shock this may well be.

Sometimes, the boy in blue or butternut was so exhausted that the idea of using an anesthetic was strictly academic. Stories are told of how a fellow would simply lean back and let the bloody operator saw away, telling the anesthetist to save his sweet-smelling potion for those who came in screaming.

Surgery in the field (where the bulk of it was done) was very much the same on both sides, the dearth of first rate surgical instruments among the Confederates notwithstanding. Operations were performed on any substantial flat surface which happened to be available, a door laid upon barrels or boxes being quite typical. Tubs to catch the blood were placed nearby as were pails of water, rags, and sponges to swish away the scarlet slime when the job was done. Out-of-doors light was preferred, whether it emanated from the blazing sun or the silvery moon. Otherwise, the work had to be carried out by lantern or torchlight, a most dangerous practice in the event ether was being used. (Ether not only burns, it explodes!) Getting enough water to drink let alone wash wounds was generally impossible, the situation at Bull Run being typical. Of that battle a Federal surgeon reported: "Water, procured with great difficulty and placed in basins for the purpose of washing the wounded, was snatched up and drank by stragglers as they passed."

Although the idea was to perform surgery as far away from the field of battle as possible, this was not always the rule. Clara Barton wrote of Antietam, "The operating tables jarred and rolled until we could hardly keep the men on them, and the roar was overwhelming . . . " And even at sea there was often harassment. Surgeon Jonathan M. Foltz recalled: "A ten-inch columbiad struck our starboard bow and rolled into the place where we were operating among the wounded. It rolled under the table where I was amputating a leg . . . "

Surgical instruments used in the Civil War were often surprisingly sophisticated, particularly in the urological area. In the field, however, saws, knives, and tourniquets were the chief items. Though much is sometimes made of the shortage of instruments in the South (occasioned mainly by the ruthless Trading With the Enemy Act of 1861), the Confederate surgeons improvised with telling success. The carpenter's saw and the pen-knife, provided they were sharp, were found to do the job about as well as anything forged for the purpose by the Yankee mills. And once in awhile improvization led to improvement—a table fork for a retractor, for example.

The trade-mark of Civil War surgery was amputation. More arms and legs were chopped off in this war than in any other conflict in which the country has ever been engaged. According to Federal records, three out of four operations were amputations and there is good reason to believe the same figures obtained in the Confederacy. At Gettysburg, for an entire week, from dawn to twilight, some surgeons did nothing but cut off arms and legs. The sound of the saw, the gushing of blood, and the squeak of carts and wagons filled to the top with their hideous cargoes made a most familiar setting.

It took little effort at the time and it has been customary ever since to damn such "butchery." And there are too many stories on both sides of knife-happy surgeons not to believe that there were butchers on the loose, especially those fellows who were eager for experience. Captain Charles McIntosh of the United States Navy related after the war that his arm was amputated by a "drunken doctor who left him to himself on the ramparts." It was said some doctors were afraid to go into battle for fear of being shot from the wrong direction. For what it is worth, legend has it that younger soldiers often saved their limbs by hiding a pistol under a pillow and drawing it out at the opportune time.

A closer look at the records of both medical services, however, shows quite clearly, in theory at least, that conservative surgery was the rule and not the exception. In some respects the knife and saw may not have been used often enough. The conservative view was official in both camps. In the *Medical and Surgical History of the War of the Rebellion* we find: " . . . accepted authorities teach, with Guthrie (the British Surgeon General during the Crimean War) that an upper extremity should not be amputated for almost any accident that can happen to it from musket shot . . . or as M. Legouest said, ' . . . shot comminution of the humerus, even attended by laceration of the brachial artery does not render amputation indispensable' . . . " From the Confederate bible, *A Manual of Military Surgery,* the statement is made, " . . . Unless the bone be extremely injured . . . or the state of the patient's health be very unfavorable, attempts should always be made to preserve the upper extremity after a gunshot wound." An influential surgeon of the time, Professor Piroff, remarked quite succinctly, "The older I grow, the less I amputate."

In essence, then, it appears that in most cases if a limb were *severely* lacerated or sustained a compound fracture, off it came, and in the medical context of the era this was proper. Pyemia and osteomyelitis are blood relatives of such injuries and, as we have seen, these were maladies beyond the capabilities of Civil War medicos. Attempting to save a smashed limb by manipulation involving septic fingers and probes usually puts the patient steps closer to the grave by facilitating the dissemination of pathogens throughout the tissues. Septic surgery, however, involves a terrible risk in itself, and if the ultraconservative surgeons had left the borderline wounds alone, they might well have run up a better record to convince the radicals to restrain their saws.

Nowhere in the labyrinth of Civil War statistics does one eschew dogmatism with more force than in dealing with the matters of medicine in general and surgery in particular. In the first place, the numbers and figures relating to the Confederacy are very often nothing more than good guesses, and secondly, the reports from the field necessarily were subject to great error, occasioned by either faulty knowledge or the unadulterated chaos of battle. About the best that emerges are "trends."

According to the Official Records, the Federals sustained

174,200 shot wounds of the extremities, of which 29,980 led to amputation, and of these 7,096 died (almost always of surgical fevers) giving a fatality figure of 26 per cent for this type of surgery. With the exception of amputations at the elbow and knee, mortality tended to increase the closer to the trunk the saw was brought to bear. For example, for the lower extremity the fatality, or mortality, rates for the foot, ankle, and leg were 6 per cent, 25 per cent, and 33 per cent, respectively. The most pathetic results were encountered with ablation at the knee—58 per cent—and hip—83 per cent. Slightly better were amputations of the thigh, with a mortality rate of 54 per cent. Amputations of the upper extremities came through more successfully, for the hand, forearm, and upper arm, the rates being 3 per cent, 14 per cent, and 24 per cent, respectively.

It seems the Confederates, statistically, fared no better. Indeed, from what can be learned the fatality rates more often than not were unbelievably close, affording strong evidence that the doctors displayed about the same degree of skill and competence. Out of 3,685 amputations of the upper arm, for instance, the Federals lost 773 (21 per cent), and in one sampling the Confederates lost 95 out of 434 (22 per cent) for comparable surgery. Again, in another study, for amputations of the arm and leg the Confederates had rates of 15 per cent and 30 per cent, respectively, as again Federal figures of 14 per cent and 33 per cent. On the other hand, out of a total of 77 amputations close to the hip performed by Southern surgeons there were "only" 37 deaths (48 per cent), a figure considerably better than that just cited for the Unionists. Among those who pulled through this 50-50 proposition, interestingly, were perhaps the hardest fighting generals of the South: John Hood, wounded at Chickamauga, and Richard Ewell hit at the Second Bull Run. Fitted out with a wooden leg and strapped to the saddle, both men fought the Blue Coats with undiminished vigor right up to the very end, Dick Ewell's "wounded" wooden leg notwithstanding.

As to whether an amputation should have been *primary*

(done within forty-eight hours) or *secondary* (done after forty-eight hours), statistics strongly favor the former. Of 1,142 primary amputations of arms and legs, recorded for the Confederacy in the first three years of the fighting, there were 315 deaths (28 per cent mortality) as against 284 deaths in 546 secondary amputations (52 per cent mortality). Again, of 2,657 primary amputations of the upper arm performed by Union surgeons, there were 602 deaths (23 per cent mortality) whereas there were 416 deaths among 897 secondary amputations (46 per cent mortality). Since these figures are in line with present-day thinking (that delay gives invading bacteria a good send off on their dirty mission), they afford a measure of confidence in Civil War statistics.

The case of Private Milton Wallen, Company A, First Kentucky Cavalry, illustrates a successful but not necessarily uneventful amputation. Wallen had his arm amputated above the elbow when a prisoner in Richmond, and sometime later was admitted to a Union general hospital. The Official Records presents his case as follows: "The patient was feeble and on August 20 the stump commenced to take on an unhealthy action and by the 24th the entire stump was attacked by hospital gangrene—the flaps beings disorganized and the bone protruding. The treatment was limited to the strictest attention to hygienic measures, with an allowance of an 'abundance of the invigorating salt air from the bay.' For a few days afterward the stump was dressed with charcoal and yeast poultices and a generous diet, and an ample of ale and other stimulants given the patient. By August 30 (1863) the sloughing process was entirely arrested."

In the field, the preferred technique for cutting off an arm or leg, particularly in the Southern service, was the "guillotine" operation, performed by slicing the soft tissue to the bone just above the damaged area with a large knife and finishing the job with a hacksaw. The arteries were then clamped and tied off with oiled silk, the ends being left long enough so that days later they could be tugged loose. (The entire cross section was thus open for dressing and the wound healed by granulation.) An occasional surgeon could finish the job in two or three minutes.

The more "advanced" operators, of whom there were a fair number, sometimes did what is called a "flap job"; namely, the bone was shortened and flaps of the soft tissue brought down over the end producing a better looking stump. This required a measure of skill, however, and quite often the novice botched the job, and ended up doing a guillotine operation anyway. As the surgeons gained experience, they began to realize that the flap operation (because of the poor drainage occasioned by the skin-sealed stump) proved slower healing and prone to infection. In short, the flap job was generally out of place in the field, and probably in most general hospitals, for that matter. Besides, a successful guillotine operation could, if the patient so desired, be "revised" later on at a more opportune time. Undoubtedly, a good number of the 6,240 flap amputations recorded by the Union fell into this category. Modern surgeons use a variety of techniques to remove an arm or leg, the particular one employed depending on the circumstances.

Sometimes damaged limbs were treated by *excision* or *resection*—with equivocal results, to say the least. Excision is the cutting out of a section of bone from the shaft, whereas resection is the cutting off of the end of a bone. Commonly, the records use the terms interchangeably. For example, "excision at the shoulder," was actually a resection in that the damaged end, or head, of the humerus was cut off and the new end joined to the scapula. Although some doctors held these procedures in high esteem, not a few were skeptical. The patient usually had a longer stay in the hospital and, worse yet, sometimes ended up with a worthless limb—if he pulled through. "The forearm dangles from the false joint and is atrophied, being of less use than if injury had been the loss of the hand; disability total . . . " is a typical comment found among the cases cited in the Official Records.

Some excisions and resections were downright "disastrous." The Union fatalities for the knee and hip joint were 81 per cent and 91 per cent, respectively! Evidently, these figures appeared as startling then as now, for most surgeons reserved their artistic skills for the upper extremities, where the prognosis was considerably less negative. Altogether, the Federals performed 4,656 excisions and resections with an overall fatality rate of 28 per cent. The Confederates appear to have done better with 117 deaths out of 647 resections (18 per cent), but with this small number superiority can hardly be claimed.

Of course, in surgical matters, one could always let nature have its way and pray for the best. And many surgeons apparently did just that! Of 60,266 Federal wounds of the extremities complicated by injuries to the bone, 26,467 were treated via *expectation*, with a fatality rate of 18 per cent—as against 26 per cent for amputation (29,143 cases) and 28 per cent for excision (4,656). Although things might have been better if the surgeons had collapsed their tents and stolen away, quite likely the vast majority of amputees were saved by the saw.

Operations other than amputation, excision, and resection played a minor role in the general picture, but none the less sparked a new pace in surgery. Whereas before the war only the most courageous surgeons would have dared penetrate the skull or abdomen, afterwards there was much less hesitancy to strike out in this direction. Coupled with the postwar blessings of antiseptic methods the beginnings of modern surgery were at hand.

Penetration of the abdomen with septic instruments leads to a fatal peritonitis, and it is certainly nothing less than a miracle that an occasional laparotomy (making an incision through the abdomen) proved successful. The procedure was advocated in cases where the patient obviously had nothing to lose, but it seems most "operations" involving the belly merely involved poking back into position anything that was poking out, and hoping for the best.

Surgery involving the skull was possibly not as bad as one might expect, but certainly bad enough. Of 900 such operations performed by Federal surgeons 517 died (67 per cent mortality).

The favorite procedure was the ancient art of trephining, or penetrating the skull with a trephine (a cylindrical saw), so as to remove a portion of bone. Typical of the more harrowing goings-on in this category was the case of Private William Lowery of the Sixth Tennessee Cavalry who on October 3, 1864 received a punctured fracture of the right parietal bone from the blow of a musket: "Under chloroform . . . the surgeon trephined skull and removed circular portion . . . tip of little finger introduced and apparently there was no injury to dura mater . . . cold water compresses . . . patient restless for several days and delirious at night . . . symptoms of cerebral disturbance were thought to be favorably modified by use of extract of Canabis indica (marihuana) . . . on October 18th, an intercurrent attack of pneumonia supervened . . . on November 3rd, there were signs of cerebral hernia . . . protrusion of the cerebral substance progressed so rapidly that on November 6th it was deemed expedient to compress the mass by a bladder of ice. On November 7th paralysis of the left arm was observed. On November 16th the cerebral hernia was still further compressed by a metallic disk. Coma supervened, and the patient died on November 17, 1864 (at Gayoso Hospital) . . . "

At the other end of the spectrum was the case of A. B. Parish of the Union Quartermaster Department who received a lacerated wound of the frontal region (with fracture and depression of the frontal bone) by a kick from a horse on September 3, 1864. He was " . . . administered chloroform and the skull trephined to raise depressed portions of bone with elevator. Given tonics, stimulants, and low diet . . . patient improved and discharged from hospital—entirely cured—on October 13, 1865."

Surgery performed to correct injuries to the face proved somewhat successful, if we generally disregard what the job looked like when it was finished. Of a total of 671 operations performed in the Union army, eighty died, giving a relatively good score of 12 per cent mortality. Most importantly, face surgery brought the talents of the dentist to the fore, particularly in the Confederate medical service. Usually given the rank of hospital steward, the Southern dentist was encouraged to treat face wounds as well as to care for the teeth. An important accomplishment in this area was the invention of the interdental splint by Doctor James Bean of Atlanta to correct fractures of the maxillae, the key bones of the face and mouth. Bean's success attracted so much attention that Surgeon General Moore directed all hospitals to set aside a ward to employ the device, and finally a hospital was set up in Atlanta, the first of its kind, to perform maxillo-facial surgery. Thus, Doctors Bean and Moore did a tremendous job in elevating the fledgling profession.

Compared to the septic surgical penetration of the skull and abdomen, chest surgery seems to have fared well. Of 494 operations, the Official Records show the Union lost "only" 198, a mortality of 40 per cent. The better score is quite logical, however, if we recall that the chest is neither a fecal repository, as is the intestine, nor the seat of the nervous system, as is the skull. Too the lungs, which comprise the bulk of the space, are richly supplied with germ-fighting tissues. At Gettysburg, for example, a shell fragment passed into the right lung of nineteen-year-old Richard Phelps of the Twenty-fifth Ohio; the boy "spat up blood from July 1st to the 10th" but recovered without further incident.

Once the knife or saw had done its duty, the next move was up to the microbes. Would they attack, and moreover would they win? In general it was the patient's toughest battle, an engagement of toxins, pus, hemorrhage, fever, and terrifying convulsions pitted against mother nature. But nature could be aided, sometimes with telling success. Good food and tender care, if available, and the will to live could and would help. There were indications that victory helped too, for some surgeons noted better results when their side had won the battle.

Most signs of microbial malfeasance attending the post-operative incision were recognized for what they were, but right up to the very end, suppuration (or the discharge of pus) was looked upon in the main as a laudable act of healing. Left undisturbed, the staph thrived in their soupy environment and, with no forces working against them except the patient's white cells and humoral antibodies, set out to invade the body at large. That they were successful is historical fact.

Infection did not always bring about death via the microbial toxins or the destruction of vital organs, for often the patient died of hemorrhage as a consequence of destroyed blood vessels, an occurrence usually precipitated by the removal of the ligatures. Actually, post-operative, or *secondary*, hemorrhage was responsible for a greater loss of blood than that directly caused by the knife or conoidal ball.

If the treatment of severe bleeding calls for dramatic measures today, it was heroic then. According to one source, blood transfusions were attempted " . . . exactly twice during the war . . . one died, one lived." The latter was in divine hands to be sure.

CHAPTER X

Died of Disease

T HE War Between the States resulted in 620,000 deaths and 10,000,000 cases of sickness, to use conservative figures. The overriding element was the microbe, not the minie. Approximately 225,000 Federals and 164,000 Confederates simply "died of disease." For the first year over one-quarter of the Union army and close to one-half of the Confederate army were on sick call, and just about five times as many died of disease as of wounds on both sides. Though the sickness rate tended to improve in the North, in the South the shortage of food, medicines, clothing, and shelter did much to break the camel's back.

The reasons for this wholesale morbidity and mortality were many, not the least being the recruiting system itself. The cry to "save the Union" in the North and to "break it" in the South was an electrifying ring carried far and wide by the greatest war songs of all time. Everybody wanted to do his bit and who were the examining doctors to stand in the way! In brief, unless one was *noticeably* in poor health, the door was wide open. It was wide open during the first years of the war because of sheer laxity, and during the latter years because of the expenditures in battle. From May, 1864 to June, 1864—a time when the machine should have been slowing down—the South had 35,000 casualties and the North almost 70,000!

Based on a report by the medical director of the Union's Army of the Potomac, three-quarters of the men discharged during the first year were adjudged as being "diseased" at the time of enlistment. The situation finally became so desperate in this regard the Surgeon General demanded and got better physicals. Inspectors were sent to the states to supervise examinations, and recruits entering camp were re-examined just to make sure. This did improve matters and for the Union the chaos of 1861 would not be repeated.

But such was by no means the picture in the Confederacy,

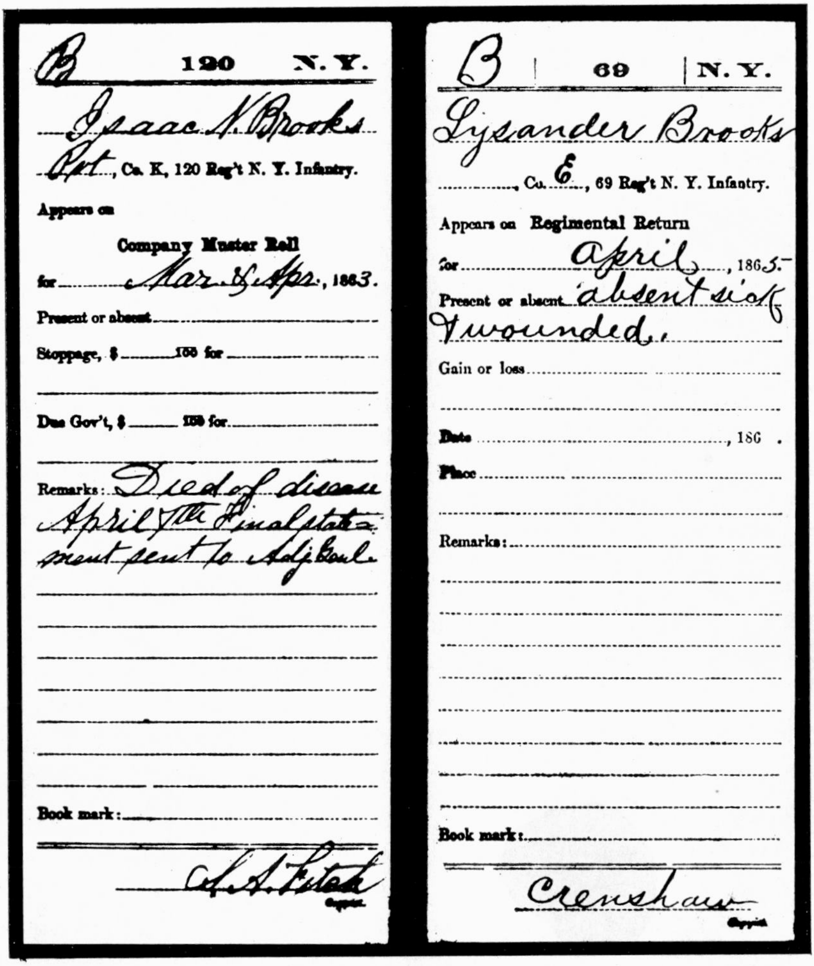

B 120 N.Y.

Isaac N. Brooks

Pvt, Co. K, 120 Reg't N. Y. Infantry.

Appears on

Company Muster Roll

for Mar. & Apr., 1863.

Present or absent

Stoppage, $ 100 for

Due Gov't, $ 100 for

Remarks: Died of disease April 7th Final statement sent to Adj Genl.

Book mark:

A. A. Fitch
Copyist.

B 69 N.Y.

Lysander Brooks

Co. E, 69 Reg't N. Y. Infantry.

Appears on Regimental Return

for April, 1865.

Present or absent absent sick & wounded.

Gain or loss

Date , 186 .

Place

Remarks:

Book mark:

Crenshaw
Copyist.

Figure 20. As these muster rolls plainly show, there was little formality in regard to the nature of a sickness or the cause of death. (National Archives.)

for if the recruiting door was wide open in the North it was
off its hinges down South. Whereas Grant could lose a few
thousand men an hour and Lincoln could close the gap by
squeezing his larger population, by 1864 Jefferson Davis was
scraping the bottom of the barrel. The Conscription Act of that
year called all male Southerners between the ages of seventeen
and fifty to the colors and at the same time directed the recruiting
people to accept anyone else who could pull a trigger or stop
a minie. With the tiger at the throat, such matters as heart trouble
and epilepsy are strictly academic.

In the beginning, and to an unhealthy extent throughout the
war, the typical inductee on arriving in camp felt as free as a bird
and lived like one. Few recruits bothered to use the slit-trench
latrines (and those who did usually forgot to shovel dirt over
the feces) and most urinated just outside the tent—and after
sundown, in the street. Garbage was everywhere, rats abounded,
and dead cats and dogs turned up in the strangest places. The
emanations of slaughtered cattle and kitchen offal together with
the noxious effluvia from the seething latrines and infested tents
produced an olfactory sensation which has yet to be duplicated
in the Western Hemisphere.

As for water—and seldom was there enough—any source
would do in the early camps. Frequently, it was so muddy and
fetid the men held their noses when they drank the stuff.
In many instances, the heavy rains washed fecal material directly
into the supply with disastrous consequences. However, in time,
water came to be regarded generally as a source of disease and
attempts were made to secure wholesome supplies. The better
outfits even progressed to the point of boiling befouled water—
visibly befouled of course.

The United States Sanitary Commission was not long in
recognizing these deplorable conditions as a threat to the Cause
and dedicated itself to their eradication. By placing the matter
squarely before the public and military, it paved the way for
the institution of corrective measures relating to sanitation and

hygiene. The Commission insisted that the bulk of sickness stemmed from filthy army installations and in no uncertain terms held the regimental brass responsible. Above all, it carried through with its proposals and admonitions via publications and workers and inspectors in the field. Nothing of such force was operative among the Southern armies, nevertheless some improvements was to be noted when conditions permitted. Although the camps tended to improve, it is open to question whether the same can be said of personal hygiene. The shortage of water and soap notwithstanding, this was mainly a case of poor education, carelessness, ignorance or, perhaps more to the point, the rural ways of the time. Among the officers, who usually represented the aristocracy, the rate of sicknes often ran *one-half* that of the enlisted men. Again, the sickness rate for the Western theater—among the men of the frontier—tended to run double that of the Eastern.

The salutary effects of good sanitation and hygiene are severely compromised in the face of poor nutrition, and bad food was the rule. Usually, it was bad to start with, and if it were not, the greasy frying pan made it that way. In almost all instances, the men did their own cooking, and poor cooks they were. Beans, oversalted meat, hardtack, flour, corn meal, rice, and vile coffee just about covered the situation on both sides of the line. Fresh fruit and vegetables were seldom seen, and anyway did not appeal to the boys as much as a soggy piece of hardtack fried in pork grease. Desiccated (dehydrated) vegetables were sometimes available in the blue-ribbon regiments of the Union, but their nickname of "desecrated" tells us about all we need to know of these items. The poorest conditions, understandably, prevailed in the Confederacy, where often the worst of the aforementioned victuals were not to be had. Sometimes horse meat and ant-infested corn meal had to do. These were luxury items compared to the bill of fare at the siege of Vicksburg, where during the final weeks "Johnny Reb" ate fried dogs, boiled cats, and roasted wharf rats.

The only bright light in this dark picture was the practice

of foraging carried on by both armies in the South. Cows were taken away on the hoof, chickens were decapitated on the spot, larders were sacked, and wine chests drained. Yet, there was a limit to this sort of thing and during the last year of the war the civilians fared little better than the menfolk in arms.

Often the shortage of food, wholesome or otherwise, resulted from red tape, incompetence, and downright dishonesty. For example, an investigation of the Union hospital at Falmouth during the winter of 1863 disclosed that the patients were getting the same food as the men in camp—salt pork, hardtack, and coffee—while at nearby Aquia Creek, the warehouses were filled to the brim with vegetables, fruit, chickens, pork and beef. Apparently, no one had the authority to put through the necessary papers. There was much of this sort going on when Joseph Hooker took over the command of the Army of the Potomac from the helpless General Burnside, and it is to Hooker's credit that nutrition was given a considerable boost. Commented one veteran, "From the commissary came less whiskey for the officers and better rations—including vegetables . . . " Moreover, General Hooker ordered the officers under his command to make certain the troops had three meals a day prepared by cooks who knew something about cooking.

The relationship between sickness and nutrition, if poorly understood by the man who signed his name with an "X," was well-appreciated by the doctors and nurses. Indeed, most illness was looked upon as being directly or indirectly tied up with, as the surgeons called it, "scorbutic diathesis," a fancy piece of Civil War nomenclature applied to scurvy or malnutrition. In the hospital, the procurement of wholesome food was pressed for with the same enthusiasm as the eradication of miasmas. Elaborate efforts were made to tailor the diet to a particular condition. This was good for the blood, that for the liver, and so on. Such expressions as "low diet," "high diet," and "stimulating food" serve to underscore the fact that here at least was one area where medicine appears to have been on the right track. True, oysters and cream can not squelch a bad case of blood poisoning, but on the other hand, they do not make it worse. In sum, good food gives nature something to fight with, and the patient something to live for.

And there were other considerations, such as the elements. A man with a bad heart might be lucky enough to beat the polluted water, vermin, and rancid grease, but not lucky enough to survive the blistering sun or icy rains. Although the Union troops were far from being well-protected against such conditions, the Confederates had just this side of nothing. At the half-way mark, entire Southern regiments were without stockings, shoes, and tents, some men taking dogs to bed with them to keep from freezing to death. Alas, ball and canister were not always guilty, for sometimes the fresh marks upon the frozen ground came simply from lacerated, bleeding feet.

Infected and frostbitten parts could be sawed off, sometimes successfully, but what about the effluvias and miasmas of the raw, damp air? They were not good to be sure. Fairly reliable reports indicate that the North had a bronchitis-pneumonia morbidity rate of 190 per 1,000 cases while the rate among the Confederates was 400 per 1,000! Once again, we see the enemy was not always in blue or gray.

Those forces working against the man who bore arms were neatly brought together and triply distilled in the prison camps, an area in which both sides sometimes threw away the book. True, certain conditions could not have been helped, but it is impossible to read the day by day records of these festered death mills without sensing a degree of calculation. According to the Adjutant General's report following the war, 19,060 Confederates died in Union prisons and 26,168 Federals died in Southern prisons. This statistic, though, does not come into full bloom until we take into account the number of men impaled and then strike a ratio. At Andersonville, for example, the death rate was 793 per 1,000 inmates and at Elmira, the North's Buchenwald, of each 1,000 held prisoner, disease killed 441 men.

But when all is said and done and knowing what we do today, should we be struck by the appalling number who died or the unbelievable number who *survived?*

CHAPTER XI

Fluxes and Fevers

T HE great abdominal cavity contains an armful of squirming musculomembranous tubing called the intestine, which, by its rectumward propulsive movement, carries a meal a distance of some twenty-odd feet for the purpose of introducing nutrients and water into the bloodstream. Considering the structure's tremendous exposure to the ingested myriad noxious chemicals and microbial agents, there is little wonder it commonly becomes an avenue of turmoil, infection, and disease.

That all is not well along this passageway is generally signaled by no stools or too many stools, the latter, the drug advertizers to the contrary, often constituting the more serious threat to life. Whether called "diarrhea," "dysentery," "looseness of the bowels," the "runs," the "G.I.'s," or, to use the nomenclature of the Rebellion, the *alvine flux,* the underlying factor relates to irritation and excessive peristalsis. The "looseness" stems from the fast trip through the tract, resulting in insufficient time for the absorption of water into the blood. Also, there is a loss of minerals vital to the body's chemical welfare.

Although these losses can of themselves cause death if not replaced, in the more vicious fluxes the initial diarrhea is merely a prelude to the wholesale destruction of the intestine itself. Ulceration ensues, blood oozes into the intestine, and the microbe enters the circulation to be carried far and wide throughout the body. When all this happens, the cause of death is obviously a concert of interrelated derangements.

The alvine fluxes reigned supreme in the Civil War's king-

Figure 21. Embalming surgeon (Union) working on soldier's body. The setup of a door supported by two barrels was also commonly used as an operating table. (Library of Congress.)

dom of misery, causing more sickness and death than any other agent or force. Considering the "G.I.'s" were not an infrequent complaint of the last Great War, we have some idea of what it must have been like a hundred years ago. One thing was certain, constipation was a luxury both North and South and, as one might expect, even more so in the Confederacy. According to the surgeon general's report, the annual morbidity rates for diarrhea and dysentery per 1,000 (of mean aggregate strength) were 543 among the Federals, and 987 among the Confederates; and the total number of deaths reached at least the 60,000 mark! Little wonder, then, that of the six tomes comprising the Official Records one is devoted exclusively to the matter of diarrhea.

The fluxes were as mysterious as they were deadly, and though the student pores over and over the thousand-odd pages devoted to the subject, he comes away knowing scarcely more than when he started—to wit, that millions of human beings were tortured and reduced to skin and bones by looseness of the bowels. None the less, the official pages prove fascinating reading for anyone interested in the development of medical thinking, because the doctors, particularly among the Federals, went to considerable lengths in their discussion of classification, cause, and treatment of the alvine fluxes.

Although in practice the terms "diarrhea" and "dysentery" were used interchangeably,* on paper the surgeon general applied the former to "all cases of flux in which frequent stools are *unaccompanied* by marked tenesmus (straining) " and the latter, to "all cases of flux in which frequent stools *are* accompanied by marked tenesmus." This pretty much agrees with Dorland's *Medical Dictionary,* which defines diarrhea as an "abnormal frequency and liquidity of fecal discharges," and dysentery as a "disorder marked by inflammation of the intestines, especially the colon, and attended by pain in the abdomen, tenesmus, and frequent stools containing blood and mucus."

Further, a flux was characterized as acute or chronic. And here we get a little better idea of the true story, for the big killer was *chronic* diarrhea, a condition at that time defined as a "chronic flux with or without tenesmus." To be "consistent," the medicos also labeled it chronic dysentery. In sum, what really mattered was whether a case of flux cleared up or not, for if it did not the patient's days were surely numbered.

There are an endless number and variety of chemical agents and microbes capable of provoking looseness of the bowels, but from what we know today a great many of the chronic diarrheas and dysenteries of the Civil War were probably *amebic* dysentery and *bacillary* dysentery, specific infections caused by specific

*Refer to second paragraph of "Introductory Note," p. 125.

microbes. Amebic dysentery, or amebiasis, is caused by a one-celled animal *(Entamoeba histolytica)* which abounds under unsanitary conditions and makes its way into the body in contaminated food and water. It sets up residence in the lining of the intestine—bringing about marked inflammation, ulceration, and dysentery—and then after a time generally enters the circulation via ruptured blood vessels. As a consequence of the ungodly infestation, abscesses are produced throughout the body, those of the liver, lungs, and brain being rapidly fatal. With the very best therapy, prognosis even today is not good in advanced cases, particularly those where the damage has already been done.

Bacillary dysentery is caused by certain bacteria (the *shigellae*) which not surprisingly turn up in areas where there is overcrowding and poor sanitation. In contrast to amebic dysentery the infection tends to remain pretty much localized, but even so the extreme loss of blood and fluid can cause death, especially if the patient was in shaky health at the start.

Of course, this by no means excludes other possibilities in the killer category. Certain viruses, for instance, have been isolated in dysentery-like infections, as have such bacterial tribes as the *salmonellae*. Although not common today, there were many cases of *intestinal* tuberculosis during the Civil War incited by contaminated food and milk, especially the latter. For example, an autopsy of Private John Schroeder, Second Maryland Volunteers, who suffered from a two-months bout of chronic diarrhea, disclosed adhesions of the left lung and "numerous ulcers of the colon, some penetrating to the peritoneal coat."

The usual causes of *acute* diarrhea—namely, improper diet, "enteric" staph, and "mild" viruses—were common enough to be chronic. Perhaps, then, Surgeon General Barnes' remarks in the Official Records can hardly be improved upon: "A careful survey of the evidence seems fully to justify the belief that these diseases (the fluxes) generally result from the simultaneous action upon large numbers of men of several of the predisposing and existing causes which have been discussed—some of the most dangerous of which are contaminated drinking water, insufficient or faulty alimentation, camp filth, especially human excreta . . . "

Be that as it may, if the flux did not do a man in, the treatment often would. Typical was Case 123. Private John Leopold, Company B, Seventy-fourth Pennsylvania Volunteers, entered the South Street Hospital in Philadelphia on October 12, 1863 with chronic diarrhea of three months standing. His self diagnosis was immediately confirmed and intensive therapy instituted. Leopold was dosed with lead acetate, opium, aromatic sulfuric acid, tincture of opium, silver nitrate, belladonna, calomel, and ipecac. However, these medicaments were "without benefit" and the coup de grâce was administered in the form of a steaming mustard plaster. Private Leopold passed away on October 26th.

A look at the above treatment discloses a mixture of the sublime along with the ridiculous. Whereas lead acetate, sulfuric acid, calomel, and silver nitrate bear about the same relationship to diarrhea as gasoline to a blazing fire, belladonna and opium are quite effective in checking diarrhea—a fact well-appreciated by anyone who has ever taken a dose of paregoric, opium being the active constituent. Tincture of opium and paregoric were always available, but nowhere in the records does one get the impression that they were used routinely in the management of the fluxes. Commonly, though, both were used in the manner just described, namely, along with agents having the opposite action. True, paregoric has no bearing upon the underlying cause, but it does stop the colic and loss of vital fluid, and sometimes this is good enough. Also, it permits a respite from straddling a slit trench all day long, an experience which must be undergone to be understood and one which Dante surprisingly overlooked.

The modern treatment for the fluxes includes the use of paregoric, adsorbent clays, and the like, in simple diarrhea, and tailor-made anti-infectives in such infections as amebic and bacillary dysenteries. A few doses of sulfadiazine in bacillary dysentery, for example, puts the patient on the road to recovery in a very short time.

In terms of a *specific* infectious disease, that is, one caused by a *specific* microorganism, typhoid fever was the chief single cause of death in both armies—taking the life of 30,000 Federals alone. Classified at the time as one of the "continued fevers," typhoid is caused by a hairy, rod-shaped bacterium *(Salmonella typhosa)* which gains entrance into the body by way of contaminated food and water. Perhaps the most insidious thing about the infection is the so-called *carrier,* the recovered individual who continues to disseminate the pathogen via feces and urine wherever he goes. Some carriers—Typhoid Mary, for instance—history records as having incited hundreds of cases. This plus the general conditions which prevailed in the camps and field easily accounts for the high incidence of this particular disease.

Because the initial stages of typhoid relate to the intestinal tract—colic, bloody diarrhea, and the like—the treatment varied little from the ordinary fluxes, with the exception perhaps of giving quinine to bring down the fever. Of course, there were the innovators. One nurse tells of managing a case of typhoid by dipping cloths into a mixture of brandy and red pepper and binding them tightly to the patient's feet, hands, and chest. Although the soldier reportedly pulled through, one would be hard put to prove the superiority of peppered brandy over Chloromycetin.

Running a close parallel to the fluxes and typhoid fever were the pneumonias or, as referred to a hundred years ago, "inflammation of the lung." Among the Federals 20,000 deaths were reported as being due to this cause, and of the 19,000 Confederates who died in Yankee prisons, 5,000 were ascribed to it. During the spring and summer of 1864 at Andersonville 350 prisoners died of the affliction. A great deal of this mortality no doubt stemmed from exposure, but most of it was simply a case of predisposing elements operating in concert, not the least of which was a pre-existing illness. All too often the patient started out with "such and such" but died of pneumonia.

This is not hard to understand considering the great number

of microbial opportunists on the one hand and the easy access to the respiratory passageways on the other. Nevertheless, most of us can put up with this situation if the body is in good order or, in the event trouble does start, if a shot or two of penicillin is available. The importance of natural resistance is dramatically undersored by the finding that the causative agent of many pneumonias *(Diplococcus pneumoniae)* is present in the throat and nasal passages of quite healthy people. But let the resistance down, and "away they go"—and went during the Civil War.

However, good food, a mustard plaster or two, and tender care did on occasion effect amazing results in stemming a case of pneumonia, for unlike the ruthless pyemias and fulminating dysenteries where the patient accelerated to the grave, here at least was an area where not all was lost at the start. There were medicaments to arrest the cough and foster expectoration, and quinine to tame a run-away fever.

Another major medical problem was malaria, a disease reportedly suffered by President Lincoln himself. This so-called "paroxysmal fever" had long been endemic and epidemic in the South, and during the first years of the war the rate of disease among the Confederate troops east of the Mississippi averaged about one case in seven. The Union medical records show a total of 1,213,685 cases of "malarial fevers" (from 1861-1866) and 12,199 deaths. The cause was generally ascribed to "miasmas emanating from stagnant waters," a theory quite consistent with the derivation of the word, malaria in Italian meaning, "bad air." The relationship of the infection—the globe's number one disease—to the Anopheles mosquito, however, did not come to light until the pioneer work of Sir Ronald Ross in 1902. Quinine was the mainstay in the treatment of the disease and although today much better antimalarial agents are available, the drug is still considered efficient in suppressing the signs and symptoms. The surgeons in both services were well-versed in its use and ranked the drug as their most valuable ally—next to the knife, that is.

There were also the much-dreaded *eruptive* fevers—smallpox, measles, scarlet fever, and erysipelas—epidemics of which at times wrought more havoc than the Springfields and Napoleons. Ordinarily these are infections of childhood, but not necessarily so among those coming from remote rural areas away from the viruses and streptococci of the cities and army camps. Not having had these infections as a child, and without the protection of vaccination, the farm boy proved a fertile field for microbial multiplication. Sometimes an entire regiment or brigade would be hit, with thousands of desperately sick men chattering with chills or burning with fever. Among the Confederates held prisoner in the North, eruptive fevers were the third ranking cause of death. These infections proved even more deadly among the Union Negro soldiers, with a mortality just about six times greater than their white brothers-in-arms.

Measles was perhaps the worst infection from a standpoint of prevalence and complications such as pneumonia and mastoiditis. Some surgeons went so far as to say that the bulk of all serious illness was traceable to this particular eruptive fever. As for smallpox, when it did hit the outcome was frightful. One hospital in Virginia reported over 1,000 deaths in a three months' period. Though vaccination was understood and generally accepted in principle, the vaccines themselves proved highly questionable, being made as they were from shed scabs. Theoretically this made sense, but in practice the scabs were often too old—losing their charge of virus—and not uncommonly contaminated. This led to infection and the appearance of large unsightly ulcers at the site of vaccination. However, an ulcer is better than smallpox, and apparently it is fair to say that vaccination, primitive though it was, did make some difference in the overall picture.

Finally we come to the diseases of indulgence. The boys have always followed the flag and the girls have always followed the boys. Of this the Civil War was a textbook picture. Prostitution was a going concern in many towns and cities and some set up shop right in camp. (On a troop train leaving from Boston, a suspicious looking major aboard turned out to be a female "recruit.") According to one Washington reporter, " (The prostitutes) fasten on to every soldier . . . who is at all susceptible and stick with the tenacity of leeches until they convey them to their haunts of iniquity . . . Quinine may be the need of the Confederate army, but copaiba* is certainly the necessity of ours." For the four years the Federal rate was 82 cases of venereal disease per 1,000 troop strength, and in the South, though no one knows for sure, it probably was as high or higher. In sum, the war was a time of disease, and as nature would have it, syphilis and gonorrhea had to join the burning fevers and lowly fluxes.

---

*A thick, yellowish-brown, spicy-smelling liquid—with an ungodly taste—used for everything under the sun, but most especially, gonorrhea.

CHAPTER XII

The Lesson

To the casual peruser of Civil War medicine, the general impression seems to be that our greatest calamity brought forth little more than hundreds of fetid hospitals and thousands of botched amputations. And yet, this is looking no farther than the end of the nose—and no pun is intended—for the serious student simply can not come away from this fascinating segment of American history without sensing the ingredients of an incipient revolution in the medical picture of the period.

The most direct and palpable effects were, not surprisingly, in military medicine in general and the United States Medical Department in particular. In Washington, there emerged a competent office of Surgeon General and in the field an efficient system of hospitals, convalescent camps, supply, sanitation, and evacuation. The Ambulance Corps established in 1864 was perhaps the single most important development and the forerunner of modern field medicine. Further, an Army Medical Museum was established—the progenitor of today's world-famous Armed Forces Institute of Pathology—and for the first time specimens were collected and studied in detail. And above all, medicine proved that instead of being a "fifth wheel to the army's coach" it was actually an essential fourth, as the World Wars were to confirm.

In matters of "pure medicine," not much appears at the first glance, but a respectable number of developments, revelations, and the like, come into focus upon close inspection. Certainly, experience was gained in handling the knife and the saw, and many surgeons were becoming less squeamish in entering the chest, abdomen, and even the cranial vault. Surgical explorations in the oral cavity, particularly in the Southern medical service, proved an integral force in the establishment of American dentistry. Anesthesia also came into its own. Its general usefulness was demonstrated beyond a doubt and its safety was, for all practical considerations, assured through the better knowledge acquired in the thousands and thousands of administrations of chloroform and ether. Furthermore, the connection between disease and microbes was beginning to be appreciated by the growing ranks of the avante guard, as was the significance of antisepsis and asepsis. At the very least, cleanliness was held in high esteem and an attempt was made to practice it by the medico worth his salt. In addition, orthopedics received quite a boost in the appearance of more practical splints and workable artificial limbs, and most particularly in the widespread use of plaster of Paris. A certain amount of interest was also being shown in the methods of rehabilitation.

But in a way these things, significant though they were, are overshadowed in retrospect by a different kind of thinking which arose from the chaos; for instance, "What went wrong?" Questions of this character strike at the essence of medical practice, and their answers are the body and soul of discovery and progress. For the first time, medical and surgical activities (including the failures) were systematically reported and analyzed, and never before had post-mortems been done on such a large scale and studied so seriously.

Turning to paramedical matters, the Rebellion gave birth to the modern hospital and American nursing. The pavilion design was rapidly incorporated into civilian institutions (the famous Boston City Hospital, to this day of pure pavilion architecture, was established as early as 1864), and the revelations of good ventilation, cleanliness, antisepsis, and wholesome food put into practice across the now *United* States, from the smallest infirmary to the most grandiose municipal establishment. Also, the Angels of the Battlefield convinced everybody—even the doctors—that the female did the best job in caring for the sick and infirm, thereby, almost overnight, catapulting the status of the nurse from pesthouse attendant to a lady of healing.

In pharmacy there was a giant step from the mortar and pestle to the elaborate coils and kettles of the pharmaceutical industry, a development which eventually would do much to make American medicine what it is today. This is not to say that the War Between the States produced any wonder drug, but rather it planted the seeds of modern day production methods and research.

Important and significant as the aforementioned factors and events proved to be, in the ultimate analysis the American Civil War first and foremost demonstrated immediately before the man in the street the true meaning of public health: bad water, bad sanitation, and bad food lead to misery and disease. The doctors were certainly convinced and a great many did something about it when they got back home. Some men distinguished themselves in this direction; for example, the famous William Williams Keen, the post-war dean of American surgery, preached the virtues of cleanliness here and abroad, and Surgeon Hunter McGuire envisioned things to come by agitating for the institution of a "National Department of Health."

Finally—and no doubt foremost even in a medical sense—there was a general recognition and acceptance of Lincoln's "charity for all" pronunciamento, a thesis placed in bold relief by Clara Barton's American National Committee (1877), which three years later became the American Red Cross.

Though the lesson of war is never worth the fee, history shows that we did learn.

Appendix

Introductory Note

Sometimes an appendix turns out to be a kind of attic— that is, a place to store but not to dwell. The author certainly hopes that such is not the case here, for a considerable amount of thought has gone into the preparation of the one at hand. This particular appendix should serve the reader as a quick refresher of basic facts and figures and, at the same time, as an embellishment of certain areas of special interest. Perhaps, too, the section *might* serve as a sort of tabular snapshot of Civil War medicine.

A word of caution: Since the bulk of the official Confederate medical records were destroyed in the great Richmond fire, the statistics in this area are often no more than educated guesses. Indeed, the experts disagree by wide margins on such basic figures as the size of the Confederate army. Moreover, one must be especially wary of the diagnoses: For instance, just what are "typho-malarial fever" and "chronic diarrhea?" In sum, the reader must always keep in mind that this was a time of *laudable pus* and *midnight miasmas*.

DEATHS FROM DISEASE AND WOUNDS OF THE MAJOR WARS*

	Disease**	Wounds***
Mexican	102	12.9
Civil War (Union)	62	13.3
Spanish American	25.6	6.1
World War I	16.5	8.1
World War II	0.6	4.5
Korean	0.5	2.5

*The Army Almanac.
**Per 1,000 strength per annum.
***Per 100 wounded.

Enlistments and Deaths

Enlistments*

UNION 2,893,304

CONFEDERACY somewhere between 1,227,890 and 1,406,180

Deaths

UNION**

    In battle 110,070

    Disease 224,586

    Accidents, suicides, etc. 24,872

        Total 359,528

CONFEDERACY**

    It battle 94,000

    Disease, etc. 164,000

        Total 258,000

TOTAL, UNION AND CONFEDERACY... 617,528

*Reducing these figures to the standard of three-year enlistments, Livermore put Union strength at 1,556,678 and Confederate strength at 1,082,119.
**Adjutant General's Officer (1885).
***Burke.

Special Causes of Death (Union) *

	Officers	Men
Killed in action	4,142	62,916
Died of wounds	2,223	40,789
Died of disease	2,795	221,791
Accidental deaths	142	3,972
Drowned	106	4,838
Murdered	37	483
Killed after capture	14	90
Suicide	26	365
Executed by U.S. authorities	x	267
Executed by the enemy	4	60
Sunstroke	5	308
Other known causes	62	1,972
Causes not stated	28	12,093
Total	9,584	349,944

Total, Officers and Men—359,528
*Adjutant General's Office (1885).

Causes of Death Among Confederate Prisoners in the North*

Of an average number of 40,815 Confederates held prisoner in the North, 18,784 died, giving a mortality for the entire war of 231 per thousand per year. (According to the Adjutant General 26,168 Union prisoners died in Southern prisons.)

Cause of Death	Total	Annual Rate Per 1,000
Typhoid-typhus	1,100	14
Malaria	1,000	13
Smallpox, measles, scarlet fever	3,500	42
Diarrhea-dysentery	6,000	73
Scurvy	351	4
Bronchitis	133	2
Inflammation of lungs	5,000	62
Other	1,700	21
	18,784	231

*Prinzing.

CAUSES OF DEATH AT ANDERSONVILLE PRISON*

Of an average of 19,060 inmates confined at the prison from March 1—August 31, 1864, 7,712 died, giving an annual death rate of 793 per 1,000.

Cause of Death	Total	Annual Rate per 1,000
Typhoid-typhus	199	20.5
Malaria	119	12.2
Smallpox, measles, scarlet fever, erysipelas	80	8.2
Diarrhea-dysentery	4,529	465.5
Scurvy	999	102.8
Bronchitis	90	9.2
Inflammation of lungs	266	27.4
Other diseases	844	86.7
Wounds	586	60.2
	7,712	792.7

*Prinzing.

WOUNDS AND SICKNESS (UNION) *

Wounds

Of the 246,712 cases of wounds reported in the Medical Records by weapons of war, 245,790 were shot wounds and 922 were sabre and bayonet.

Sickness

Of 5,825,480 admissions to sick report there were:

Cases		Deaths
75,368	typhoid	27,050
2,501	typhus	850
11,898	continued fever	147
49,871	typho-malarial fever	4,059
1,155,266	acute diarrhea	2,923
170,488	chronic diarrhea	27,558
233,812	acute dysentery	4,084
25,670	chronic dysentery	3,229
73,382	syphilis	123
95,833	gonorrhea	6
30,714	scurvy	383
3,744	delirium tremens	450
2,410	insanity	80
2,837	paralysis	231

*Official Records

AMPUTATIONS (UNION) *
(29,980 Reported Cases)

	Cases	Deaths	Per Cent Fatality
Fingers	7,902	198	3
Forearm	1,761	245	14
Upper arm	5,540	1,273	24
Toes	1,519	81	6
Leg	5,523	1,790	33
Amputation at thigh	6,369	3,411	54
" at knee joint	195	111	58
" at hip joint	66	55	83
" at ankle joint	161	119	74

*Official Records.

CLASSIFICATION OF DISEASE ACCORDING TO
UNION MEDICAL DEPARTMENT*

Class I   Zymotic**
            Order 1. Miasmotic***
            Order 2. Enthetic****
            Order 3. Dietic (food)
Class II   Constitutional*****
            Order 1. Diathetic
            Order 2. Tubercular
Class III   Parasitic (Worm Infestation)
Class IV   Local
            Order 1. Nervous
            Order 2. Eye
            Order 3. Ear
            Order 4. Organs of Circulation
            Order 5. Organs of Respiration
            Order 6. Digestive Organs
            Order 7. Urinary and Genital Organs
            Order 8. Bones and Joints
            Order 9. Integumentary System
Class V   Wounds, Accidents and Injuries
            Order 1. Wounds, Accidents and Injuries
            Order 2. Homicide
            Order 3. Suicide
            Order 4. Execution

*Adopted by the U.S.A. Medical Department from Dr. William Farr of the English Army (Crimean War).
**"Epidemic, endemic or contagious 'affections' induced by some specific body or by anomalies in the quantity or quality of food."
***"Affections due to various atmospheric influences, such as products of vegetable and animal decomposition, specific emanations from the human body in a state of disease and the so-called marsh miasms."
****"Diseases transmitted by the inoculation of morbid matter."
*****"Sporadic affections often hereditary and generally involving several organs, in which morbid products or new formations frequently make their appearance."

CLASSIFICATION OF DISEASE ACCORDING TO
CSA MEDICAL DEPARTMENT*

   I.   Fevers.
  II.   Diseases of the digestive system.
 III.   Diseases of the respiratory system.
  IV.   Diseases of the circulatory system.
   V.   Diseases of the brain and nervous system.
  VI.   Diseases of the urinary and genital organs and venereal "affections."
 VII.   Diseases of the serous exhalent vessels.
VIII.   Diseases of the fibrous and muscular structures.
  IX.   Abscesses and ulcers.
   X.   Diseases of the eye.
  XI.   Diseases of the ear.
 XII.   Other diseases (twenty-three ailments, altogether), e.g.,
        Debilitas.
        Nostalgia.
        Scorbutus.

*Official Records.

The Fluxes*

I. Classification. The fluxes, which in the "master" classification apparently belonged to Class IV, Order 6, were further classified and characterized as follows:
 - A. Acute diarrhea: All cases of flux in which frequent stools are unaccompanied by marked tenesmus.
 - B. Acute dysentery: Above plus tenesmus (straining) .
 - C. Chronic dysentery: Chronic fluxes, or "chronic diarrhea" whether tenesmus is present or not.
 - D. Tubercular diarrhea: All cases of flux connected with tubercular ulceration.

II. Causes of Fluxes.
 - A. Faulty alimentation: Bad food, alcohol, errors of diet.
 - B. Dyspeptic conditions and constipation.
 - C. Portal congestion.
 - D. Meteorlogical conditions.
 - E. Endemic and epidemic influences.
 - F. Contagion.

III. Treatment of Fluxes.
 - A. Diet (e.g., forinaceous articles of food) .
 - B. Venesection.
 - C. Medication.
   - (1) Emetics.
   - (2) Purgatives.
   - (3) Diaphoretics.
   - (4) Diuretics.
   - (5) Opium.
   - (6) Anodynes.
   - (7) Hypnotics.
   - (8) Astringents.
   - (9) Tonics (vegetable) .
   - (10) Turpentine.
   - (11) Bromine. ·
   - (12) Iodine.
   - (13) Antiseptic remedies.

*The entire Part II of Volume I of the Official Records is devoted to the fluxes (i.e., diarrhea and dysentery) , the principal "complaint" of the Civil War.

"Consolidated Statement of Articles of Medical and Hospital Property Carried with the Army of the Potomac Across the Rapidan (May 4, 1864) ."*

Drugs

Acacia	Ferric chloride
Sulfuric acid	Mercury pills
Tannic acid	Morphine
Tartaric acid	Olive oil
Ether	Castor oil
Alcohol	Turpentine
Alum	Opium
Ammonium carbonate	Whiskey
Ammonia water	Brandy
Spirits of Ammonia	Lead acetate
Silver nitrate	Potassium arsenite
Camphor	Potassium iodide
Cantharides	Quinine
Chloroform (35 quarts)	Liquid soap
Collodion	Squill

*Official Records.

Drugs

Creosote
Belladonna
Ipecac
Epsom salt
Mustard
Copaiba

Rochelle salt
Tarragonna wine
Rum
Iodine
Colchicine

Hospital Stores

Beef stock
Candles
Farina
Nutmegs
Sugar
Tea

Condensed milk
Canned peaches
Corn starch
Jellies
Lemons
Dried fruit

Dressings, Etc.

Adhesive plasters
Binder boards
Cotton bats
Cotton wadding
Flannel
Gelatine plasters
Lint
Muslin

Splints
Sponge
Medical chests
Medical panniers
Hospital knapsacks
Buckets
Surgeon's silk
Tents

U.S. ARMY MEDICINE PANNIER (SQUIBB) *

Following are the medicines contained in the pannier; the bottles and vials themselves bore no markings save the identification number (here given) on the top of the cork.

1. Cantharides
2. Silver nitrate
3. Silver chloride
4. Iodine
5. Tartar emetic
6. Mercurous chloride
7. Beef extract
8. Coffee extract
9. Condensed milk
10. Black tea
11. Alcohol
12. Spirit of nitrous ether
13. Strong alcohol
14. Cough mixture
15. White sugar
16. Chloroform
17. Liniment
18. Syrup of squill
19. Ammonia water
20. Compound spirit of ether
21. Tincture of opium
22. Fluidextract of cinchona
23. Fluidextract of valerian
24. Fluidextract of ginger
25. Olive oil
26. Oil of turpentine

27. Glycerine
28. Paregoric
29. Solution of ferric sulfate
30. Aromatic spirit of ammonia
31. Compound cathartic pills
32. Pills of colocynth and ipecac
33. Ipecac and opium powder
34. Quinine sulfate
35. Potassium chlorate
36. Potassium bicarbonate
37. Potassium iodide
38. Rochelle salt
39. Morphine sulfate
40. Pills of camphor and opium
41. Mercury pills
42. Opium pills
43. Tannic acid
44. Alum
45. Collodion
46. Cresote
47. Fluidextract of aconite
48. Fluidextract of colchicine
49. Fluidextract of ipecac
50. Tincture of ferric chloride
51. Lead acetate
52. Zinc sulfate

*Smith.

*Official Records.

Autenrieth Medicine Wagon*

The Autenrieth was the most popular of the medicine wagons. In addition to seventy-six medicinal preparations (which were of the same character as Squibb's pannier), the completely stocked wagon contained the following:

Hospital Stores
Arrowroot
Candles
Extract of beef
Extract of coffee
Farina
Nutmegs
Crushed sugar
Black tea

Instruments
Bucks' sponge-holder
Cupping tins
Lancets
Pocket case
Probangs
Scarificators
Scissors
Stethoscope
Syringes
Teeth extracting instruments
Tongue depresser
Tourniquets
Trusses

Books
U.S. Dispensatory
Surgery, Sargent's Minor
Gunshot Wounds, Longmore's

Dressings
Adhesive plaster
Binder's board
Cotton bats
Cotton wadding
Flannel, red
Gilta-percha cloth
Ichthyocolla plaster
Lint, patent
Lint, scraped
Muslin
Needles
Oiled muslin
Oiled silk
Pencils
Pins
Rolled bandages
Silk
Splints

Furniture
Basins
Bed pan
Buckets
Corks
Corkscrew
Funnel
Grater, nutmeg
Hatchet
Hone and strap
Lanterns, glass
Measures
Medicinal measuring glasses
Mill, coffee
Mortar and pestle
Pill boxes
Pill tile
Razor and strap
Scales and weights
Sheepskin
Spatulas
Urinals
Vials
Matches
Tin scoops

Confederate Medicine Wagon*

Acetic acid
Adhesive plaster
Alcohol
Aloes
Ammonia water
Arsenic oxide
Assafoetida

Columbo
Copaiba
Creosote
Digitalis
Ether
Hydrochloric acid
Hyoscyamus

Morphine sulfate
Opium
Quinine sulphate
Rhubarb
Senna
Sugar
Sulfuric acid

*Official Records.

CONFEDERATE MEDICINE WAGON
(*cont'd.*)

Belladonna extract	Iodine	Strychnine
Calomel	Jalap	Tartaric acid
Camphor	Magnesium oxide	Valerian
Cantharides	Mercuric Chloride	
Chloroform	Mercury ointment	

CASUALITIES IN MAJOR BATTLES*

	Federal	Confederate
First Bull Run, Va. (July 21, 1861)	2,645	1,981
Fort Donelson, Tenn. (February 12-16, 1862)	2,832	16,623
Shilo, Tenn. (April 6-7, 1862)	13,047	10,694
Fair Oaks or Seven Pines, Va. (May 31-June 1, 1862)	5,031	6,134
Seven Days' Battle, Va. (Peninsular Campaign) (June 25- July 1, 1862)	15,849	17,136
Second Bull Run, Va. (August 29-30, 1862)	14,754	8,397
Harper's Ferry, W. Va. (September 12-15, 1862)	11,783	500
Antietam (Sharpsburg), Md. (September 17, 1862)	12,410	13,724
Perryville, Ky. (October 8, 1862)	4,211	3,396
Fredericksburg, Va. (December 13, 1862)	12,653	5,309
Murfreesboro or Stone's River, Tenn. (December 1, 1862-January 2, 1863)	12,906	11,739
Chancellorsville, Va. (May 1-5, 1863)	16,792	12,764
Siege of Vicksburg, Miss. (May 18-July 4, 1863)	8,873	39,491
Gettysburg, Pa. (July 1-3, 1863)		
Engaged	88,289	75,000
Killed	3,155	3,903
Wounded	14,529	18,735
Missing	5,365	5,425
Total losses	23,049	28,063
Chickamauga, Ga. (September 10-21, 1863)	16,170	18,454
Chattanooga Engagements (Tenn.) (November 23-25, 1863)	5,824	6,667
The Wilderness, Va. (May 5-7, 1864)	17,666	7,750
Spotsylvania Court House, Va. (May 8-20, 1864)	18,399	9,500
Cold Harbor, Va. (June 1-3, 1864)	12,000	unknown
Siege of Petersburg, Va. (June 10-April 2, 1864)	42,000	28,000
Atlanta, Ga. (July 22, 1864)	3,722	8,500
Sayler's Creek, Va. (April 6, 1865)	1,180	7,000

*Livermore.

THE REGIMENT

The regiment was the "basic unit" of the Union and Confederate armies and, for all practical purposes, its organization was the same on both sides. All told, the North raised, according to Fox, the equivalent of 2,047 regiments and the South, 764. The officers and noncommissioned officers stationed at regimental headquarters were as follows:

Officers
- Colonel
- Lieutenant Colonel
- Major
- Adjutant
- Quartermaster
- Surgeon
- Two Assistant Surgeons
- Chaplain

Noncommissioned Officers
- Sergeant Major
- Quartermaster Sergeant
- Commissary Sergeant
- Hospital Steward
- Two musicians

Bibliography

The technical aspects and central considerations of this book, in the main, have been fashioned about the indispensable *Medical and Surgical History of the War of the Rebellion* ("Official Records") and the author's own researches and writings in medical science, in particular his *Basic Facts of Medical Microbiology* and *Basic Facts of Pharmacology*. And as a general guide to the literature of nontechnical and peripheral matters, much reliance was placed upon Cunningham's *Doctors in Gray* and Adam's *Doctors in Blue*, possibly the best researched books available on the overall details. Other references of special usefulness were Smith's *Medicine for the Union Army*, Franke's *Pharmaceutical Conditions and Drug Supply in the Confederacy*, Boatner's *Civil War Dictionary* and Kelly's *Dictionary of American Medical Biography*. Noteworthy too, are such superbly fascinating classics as John Billing's *Hardtack and Coffee* and Louisa May Alcott's *Hospital Sketches*. The works consulted follow.

Adams, George W.: *Doctors in Blue*. New York, Henry Schuman, 1952.

Alcott, Louisa M.: *Hospital Sketches*. Boston, James Redpath, 1863.

The Army Almanac. 2nd Ed. Harrisburg, The Stacpole Co., 1959.

Ashburn, P. M.: *A History of the Medical Department of the United States*. Boston, Houghton Mifflin Co., 1929.

Austin, Anne L.: *History of Nursing Source Book*. New York, G. P. Putnam's Sons, 1957.

Babcock, W. W.: Bromine water. *J. A. M. A., 129*:1094, 1945.

Battles and Leaders of the Civil War. Ned Bradford, Editor. New York, Appleton-Century-Crofts, Inc., 1956.

Bettmann, Otto L.: *A Pictorial History of Medicine*. Springfield, Thomas, 1956.

Billings, John D.: *Hardtack and Coffee*. Boston, G. M. Smith, 1887.

Boatner, Mark M.: *The Civil War Dictionary*. New York, David McKay Co., Inc., 1959.

Brinton, John H.: *Personal Memoirs*. New York, The Neale Publishing Co., 1914.

Brooks, S. M.: *Basic Facts of Pharmacology*, 2nd Ed. Philadelphia, W. B. Saunders Co., 1963.

——————: *Basic Facts of Medical Microbiology*. 2nd Ed. Philadelphia, W. B. Saunders Co., 1962.

Bucklin, Sophronia E.: *In Hospital and Camp: A Woman's Record of Thrilling Incidents Among the Wounded in the Late War*. Philadelphia, J. E. Potter and Co., 1869.

Bullough, Bonnie, and Bullough, Vern: The origins of modern American nursing: the Civil War era. *Nurs. Forum, 2* (No. 2) :12, 1963.

Burdett, Henry C.: *Hospitals and Asylums of the World*. Vol. III. London, J. A. Churchill, 1893.

Castiglioni, Arturo: *A History of Medicine*. 2nd Ed. New York, Alfred Knopf. 1947.

Catton, Bruce: *This Hallowed Ground*. Garden City, Doubleday and Co., Inc., 1956.

——————: *A Stillness at Appomattox*. Garden City, Doubleday and Co., Inc., 1953.

Cecil, Russell L., and Loeb, Robert F.: *Textbook of Medicine*, 10th Ed. Philadelphia, W. B. Saunders, 1959.

Chisolm, John J.: *Manual of Military Surgery*. Richmond, C.S.A. War Department, 1864.

The Civil War years. *J. Amer. Pharm. Ass., 1* (No. 12) :764 (December) 1961.

Coggins, Jack: *Arms and Equipment of the Civil War*. New York, Doubleday and Co., Inc., 1962.

Crawford, Samuel W.: *The Genesis of the Civil War; the Story of Sumter*. New York, C. L. Webster and Co., 1887.

Cumming, Kate: *Kate: the Journal of a Confederate Nurse*. Edited by Richard B. Harwell. Baton Rouge, Lousiana State University Press, 1959.

Cunningham, Horace H.: *Doctors in Gray*. Baton Rouge, Louisiana State University Press, 1958.

Davis, Burke: *Our Incredible Civil War*. New York, Holt, Rinehart and Winston, 1960.

Davis, Loyal: *Christopher's Textbook of Surgery*. 7th Ed. Philadelphia, W. B. Saunders Co., 1960.

Dictionary of American Biography. Edited by Allen and Dumas Malone. New York, Charles Scribner's Sons, 1930.

Dolan, Josephine A.: *Goodnow's History of Nursing*. 11th Ed. Philadelphia, W. B. Saunders Co., 1963.

Donald, D. H.: *Divided We Fought*. New York, The Macmillan Co., 1952.

Doubleday, Abner: *Reminiscences of Forts Sumter and Moultrie*. New York, Harper and Brothers, 1876.

Dowdey, Clifford: *Lee's Last Campaign*. Boston, Little Brown and Co., 1960.

Foltz, Charles: *Surgeons of the Seas*. Indianapolis, Bobbs-Merrill Co., Inc., 1931.

Fox, William F.: *Regimental Losses in the American Civil War*. Albany, Albany Publishing Co., 1889.

Franke, Norman H.: A Confederate recipe book, *Amer. J. Hospital Pharm., 17*:169 (March) 1960.

————————: *Pharmaceutical Conditions and Drug Supply in the Confederacy*. Madison, American Institute of the History of Pharmacy, 1955.

Gathercoal, Edmund N., and Wirth, Elmer H.: *Pharmacognosy*. Philadelphia, Lea and Febiger, 1947.

Goodman, L. A., and Gilman, A.: *The Pharmacological Basis of Therapeutics*. 2nd Ed. New York, The Macmillan Co., 1955.

Hart, Albert G.: The surgeon and the hospital in the Civil War. Reprinted from papers of the *Milit. Historical Soc. Mass., 13*:231 (April) 1902.

Holland, Mary A.: *Our Army Nurses*. Boston, Press of Lounsberry, Nichols, and Worth, 1897.

Jolly, Ellen R.: *Nuns of the Battlefield*. Providence, the Providence Visitor Press, 1927.

Kelly, Howard A., and Burrage, Walter L.: *Dictionary of American Medical Biography*. New York, D. Appleton Co., 1928.

Kimmel, Stanley: *Mr. Lincoln's Washington*. New York, Bramhall House, 1957.

Lee, Charles O.: The Shakers as pioneers in the American herb and drug industry. *Amer. J. of Pharm., 132*:178 (May) 1960.

Livermore, Mary A.: *My Story of the War*. Hartford, A. D. Worthington and Co., 1896.

Livermore, Thomas L.: *Numbers and Losses in the Civil War*. Boston, Houghton Mifflin and Co., 1900.

Major, Ralph H.: *A History of Medicine*. 2 Vol. Springfield, Thomas, 1954.

Maxwell, William: *The Political History of the U. S. Sanitary Commission*. New York, Longmans, Green, 1956.

McElroy, John: *This Was Andersonville*. New York, McDowell,

Oblensky, 1957.

McMaster, John B.: *A History of the People of the United States during Lincoln's Administration.* New York, D. Appleton and Co., 1927.

Meakins, Jonathan C.: *Practice of Medicine.* 6th Ed. St. Louis, C. V. Mosby Co., 1956.

The Medical and Surgical History of the War of the Rebellion. Vol. 6. Joseph K. Barnes, Editor. Washington, Government Printing Office, 1870.

Mitchell, S.: *Gunshot Wounds and Other Injuries of Nerves.* Philadelphia. J. B. Lippincott and Co., 1864.

Nineteenth century surgery. *Boston Med. Surg. J., 136*:7, 1897.

Otto, Eisenschiml: *The Hidden Face of the Civil War.* Indianapolis, Bobbs-Merrill Co., Inc., 1961.

Packard, Francis R.: *History of Medicine in the United States.* New York, Paul B. Hoeber, Inc., 1932.

Perley, Thomas F.: *War of the Rebellion,* Official Records of the Union and Confederate Armies, Series I., Vol. 21. Washington, Government Printing Office, 1863.

Phisterer, Frederick: *Statistical Record of the Armies of the United States.* New York, Charles Scribner's Sons, 1883.

Photographic History of the Civil War. New York, Review of Reviews Co., 1912.

Prinzing, Friederich: *Epidemics Resulting from Wars.* New York, Oxford Clarondon Press, 1916.

Ransom, John L.: *Andersonville.* Philadelphia, Douglass Brothers, 1883.

Ross, Ishbel: *Angel of the Battlefield.* New York, Harper and Brothers, 1956.

Smith, George W.: *Medicines for the Union Army.* Madison, American Institute of the History of Pharmacy, 1962.

Stevenson, Isobel: Medical literature of the Civil War. *CIBA Symposia, 3* (No. 2) :917, 1962.

Stille, Chas. J.: *History of the U. S. Sanitary Commission.* New York, Hurd Houghton, 1869.

Stimson, Julia C., and Thompson, Ethel C.: Women nurses with the Union forces during the Civil War. *Milit. Surg., 62*:227, (Feb.) 1928.

Surgery before antisepsis. *J. Missouri Med. Ass., 32*:169, 1935.

Swanberg, W. A.: *First Blood.* New York, Charles Scribner's Sons, 1957.

Tiffany, Francis: *Life of Dorothea Dix.* Boston, Houghton Mifflin and Co., 1890.

The U. S. Army in the Civil War. Army Information Digest, August, 1961.

Weist, J. R.: *Sketches of War History.* Cincinnati, Robert Clarke and Co., 1888.

Wiley, Bell I.: *Embattled Confederates,* New York, Harper and Row, 1964.

Woodward, Joseph J.: *The Hospital Stewards Manual.* Philadelphia, J. B. Lippincott and Co., 1863.

Wyeth, John A.: *With Sabre and Scalpel.* New York, Harper and Brothers, 1914.

Index

(Page references in *italics* denote illustrations.)